THE IMPENETRABLE SEA

BY THE SAME AUTHOR

A Tetralogy
Hand and Flower Press. 1951

The Glazier
T. Werner Laurie Ltd. 1956

The Inexplicable Sky
T. Werner Laurie Ltd. 1956
The Citadel Press, New York. 1957

Your Secret Powers
Neville Spearman Ltd. 1958

The IMPENETRABLE SEA

By
ARTHUR CONSTANCE

OLDBOURNE
LONDON

OLDBOURNE BOOK CO. LTD.
121 Fleet Street, London, E.C.4

First published 1958

© Oldbourne Book Co. Ltd., 1958

SET IN 12 POINT BASKERVILLE
AND PRINTED IN GREAT BRITAIN
BY EBENEZER BAYLIS AND SON, LTD., THE
TRINITY PRESS, WORCESTER, AND LONDON

"WHAT DO WE REALLY KNOW of the sea even today? Just that little revealed to us by nautical soundings rather limited in scope; just the animals and the objects fished up by more or less blind dredgings; and, finally, just that fragmentary information brought to the surface by divers, few of whom have ever gone below the surface with scientific intent and certainly none of whom have ever descended from a poetic urge.

No, the fact is that man must admit that quite close to his shores—practically within a few feet—an unknown world begins, a zone more secret and mysterious than any unexplored territory that ever was on dry land. And this secret world laps all our shores, covers the greater part of the maps of our world with featureless blue, contains the most astonishing and prodigious forms of animal life, and conceals the ultimate origin of all life whether on land or sea.

Even for men who live all their lives along the coasts and perhaps spend the greater part of their lives at sea, this other world is still a tremendous enigma, a sheer mass beyond the reach of our direct knowledge."

Pierre de Latil and Jean Rivoire
Man and the Underwater World
(Jarrolds. 1956)

CONTENTS

CONTENTS

LIST OF ILLUSTRATIONS

PREFACE

IN this age of progressive scientific achievement, which fosters experimental activity at the expense of contemplative meditation, we seem to be in some danger of losing our sense of wonderment. Because the miraculous has become commonplace, the commonplace has ceased to be miraculous in the sense conveyed by Whitman's words: "To me every hour of the light and dark is a miracle. Every cubic inch of space is a miracle."

Many books of recent years survey the world's oceans and describe their teeming life-forms more comprehensively than this book, and my research through numbers of them has deepened my admiration and respect for all whose scientific investigations and explorations have contributed to our knowledge of the seas. Yet the subject is so vast, and has so many ramifications, that even as the light of the sun penetrates only a little way down into the oceans (the last trace of light vanishing at 3,500 feet below the surface) so all the accumulated knowledge of man regarding the world's seas remains superficial. Beneath every carefully-acquired fact regarding any of the sea's characteristics or living creatures lie infinities of further facts: an incredibly vast realm of undiscovered truth comparable with the dark, mysterious abysses of the ocean itself, unpenetrated and virtually impenetrable.

Carlyle linked wonderment with worship in a significant passage in which he said: "The man who does not habitually wonder . . . is but a pair of spectacles behind which there is no Eye." This thought is strikingly confirmed in a sentence written by the joint authors of the first connected story of man's relationship to the sea, a quotation from which appears at the beginning of this book: "No other sources of information can ever make up for that ultimate master knowledge revealed by men's eyes, or for that less tangible but even profounder knowledge attained emotionally by the soul of man rather than his mind."

If this book increases a sense of wonderment in its readers' minds regarding the sea, in the sense indicated by these quotations, its purpose will be fulfilled.

I must express my sincere gratitude to Frank W. Lane, author of that monumental and fascinating book *Kingdom of the Octopus*, for checking my chapter on the cephalopods. My thanks are also due to Mr. H. A. Humphrey of the Oldbourne Press for creative criticism; to correspondents in several countries (particularly Fletcher King of Florida and others in the U.S.A.) for news clippings; and especially to my wife for her invaluable help in reading the MS. of this book.

27 *Clarence Parade*   ARTHUR CONSTANCE
Cheltenham, England

CHAPTER I

INTO THE DEPTHS

THEY were awake at 6.30 a.m. on that momentous 14th of February, 1954. The sea was heaving and tossing restlessly as though it resented what they were about to do. Over two and a half miles of dark swirling water lay below the *Élie Monnier's* keel as she rolled and pitched with the motion of the waves. Commander Houot and Lieutenant Willm (who were about to make another descent in the bathyscaphe F.R.N.S.3, 160 miles south-west of Dakar, French West Africa) made a hasty breakfast, checked their asdic signals, shook hands with the others, and jumped down into the dinghy which had been put over the side.

The boat rose and sank in the swell as they went across to the F.R.N.S.3. The upper structure, or float, of the "deep boat" lay on the heaving water like a surfaced submarine. Suspended from its belly was the ten-ton steel sphere which was to be their "cabin" during the descent. Grey mist shrouded the horizon and blotted out the dunes on the coastline. Only the *Mamelles*, the twin "Paps of Dakar", emerged remote and ghost-like from the haze.

They reached the float, gained the bridge, and opened the air-lock hatch. The divers, who had just come aboard, received their orders and went over the side, holding their boat-hooks, to make their final inspection. There were, as always, last-moment difficulties, but these were quickly overcome. The tow-line was cast off. To Willm, who had gone ahead into the sphere, came the statement

13

over the phone that all the vents were opened. Those above the two men, on deck, moved to the dinghy and cast off from the bathyscaphe. In a few moments all personnel were away from the float.

Inside the submerged sphere, Willm informed the *Élie Monnier* that they were ready to dive. Back came the instruction from Commander Tailliez, supervising the operation: "Hello, bathyscaphe, you may dive."

Houot—still in the upper structure—dashed for the porthole of the hatch. Sea water was already swilling over it. He went through into the steel ball—over six feet in diameter, with a shell varying from 3 to 6 inches—and closed the hatch. The two men took their positions at the controls, watching the gauges. Over the radio-telephone came the words: "Your deck is going under."

The needles of the vertical-speed log jerked spas-modically and then settled down to their registration, showing that the blades of the instrument were already turning. The dive had begun. Willm read off the metres: "Seven—eight—nine—ten." Two-way communication was cut as the bathyscaphe left the surface at 10.8 a.m. While surfaced it had been possible by radio-telephone. It still remained possible to send signals upward—not speech. But no messages or signals of any kind could come down to them through the intervening water, upon the surface of which only a widening patch of fluorescent green now remained to show where the bathyscaphe had rested.

Houot and Willm were now suspended in their steel sphere from a float carrying over 17,000 gallons of petrol in twelve tanks, and several tons of lead and steel shot, their controls enabling them to regulate the speed of the entire structure's descent or ascent. Isolated from the world above them, as they sank into the abyss, they continually tapped out signals on the asdic key, but had no means of knowing whether or not they were received by the *Élie Monnier* above them.

They went down into a world seething with plankton
—multitudes of small crustaceans and other sea creatures
which (as seen through the perspex porthole) drifted upwards in swarms like a snowstorm in reverse. Strongly
illuminated by the light which streamed through the
porthole from one of two powerful searchlights, the
planktonic multitude rushed here and there, drew nearer
or receded, as they were left behind by the bathyscaphe's
descent, but their background was one of black and
mysterious stillness. Houot worked the camera as their
steel cabin went spiralling down.

By 10.40 a.m. they had reached a depth of 400 metres—
roughly 1,200 feet in 32 minutes. Now and again a few
siphonophores were glimpsed among the upward-
streaming plankton—transparent, beautifully-coloured
creatures similar to sea-anemones. One or two looked
like huge tadpoles of living light as they went
past.

There was no vibration, nor even any feeling of
motion, as Houot and Willm went down. They seemed
to be poised in a vast realm of unreality: spectators of
scenes beyond the perspex which seemed to be painted
on a vast black canvas ceaselessly unrolling upwards to
the surface of the sea, which now seemed infinitely
remote and lost to them.

Spots of water were now falling on them as they knelt
there. The enormous pressure of the waters outside was
compressing the two hemispheres of their spherical cabin
—sealing them even more tightly together and forcing
out drops of moisture from the circular joint.

They took it in turn to change their clothes. The
temperature of their strange compartment was falling
steadily.

They switched on their second floodlight at intervals—
reinforcing the one which sent its vivid beam downward
into the swirling darkness. At 3,000 feet down Houot
made a note that all forms of life had disappeared—but

he had to revise his opinion later when swarms of living creatures passed the porthole again.

By 11.30 a.m. they were over a mile down, and a few moments later they passed the greatest depth they had attained during previous descents. Above them on the surface the *Élie Monnier* was receiving their signals, and the men on her realized, with rising excitement, that they had broken their own record. Using the second floodlight, Houot saw seething clouds of plankton, and realized that he had previously been led to believe that life had ceased because myriads of the living creatures were too small to be seen with the one searchlight. But now they were seeing slightly bigger ones—what seemed to be red shrimps, with long antennae, drifted upwards in vast shoals.

They had slowed down a little. By noon they were down to nearly ten thousand feet, but still about three thousand feet from the bottom. At that depth they halted their queer craft for a while. The "rain" had stopped. The tremendous pressure of the water now crushing them down was forcing the hemispheres tightly together.

The silence was broken only by the hissing of the oxygen and the humming of the transformers. They had no need to start the bathyscaphe descending again—it started to move downwards of its own accord as the temperature of the outer waters affected the petrol within the tanks.

The pressure gauges at last registered a depth of two miles—no one in human history had ever gone so far down into the ocean.

At that depth they again saw great swarms of shrimps and siphonophores—or, as Houot described them, desiring greater accuracy: "Organisms resembling siphonophores."

Several hundred feet lower they saw a swarm of medusae: those fantastic jellyfish which resemble minia-ture umbrellas with short shafts (with mouths at the end of them) each carrying a fringe of stinging tentacles. They swim by rhythmic pulsations of their bell-like shapes, sucking in and driving out the water in a kind of "jet-propulsion". What was the nature of such creatures' lives, over two miles below the surface of the sea? How could their soft bodies withstand the terrific pressure of the water above them—pressure so great that the wall of the bathyscaphe's steel sphere had to be at least three inches thick to withstand it?

At 12,000 feet they were sinking fast. They shed ballast for twenty-five seconds, and then again for fifteen seconds, until the bathyscaphe was descending very slowly. Their echo-sounder told them that the sea-bed was near. They watched anxiously for it to appear, shed ballast again for ten seconds to slow them down even more. Suddenly, at 13,125 feet, Willm shouted, "I can see the bottom!"

The echo-sounder registered twenty metres—fifteen—ten. . . .

The guide chain had touched down. The bathyscaphe came to a stop. Under perfect control it had reached the bottom of the sea, after a journey downwards of 13,287 feet—the greatest depth ever attained by man.

In the great circle of light cast by their searchlights the ocean floor seemed to be composed of fine white sand, covered with ridges and mounds, and with holes at intervals. They switched on their two motors and cruised around horizontally for thirty-six minutes. Sixty-eight thousand tons of water now pressed upon them, doing its utmost to crush the walls of the steel sphere in which they knelt—yet their extraordinary habitation stubbornly resisted the enormous pressure and safeguarded their lives. They saw sharks down there, swimming lazily near the ocean floor—creatures which they afterwards described as quite unlike any sharks seen on the surface: monsters with enormous mouths, swimmers which seemed quite undisturbed by the light. They saw a

17

colony of small animals grouped together and attached to the sea-bottom—strange creatures not unlike sea-anemones. They watched a queer animal that looked like an enormous flower—resembling, perhaps, a tulip more than anything else—a plant-animal about a foot tall, spreading its leaf-like arms and swaying gently in the current.

Suddenly the sphere shuddered as though some huge creature had struck it. Something was happening in the float over their heads. The bathyscaphe started to ascend, and they realized what had happened—the battery cases had fallen off, and the craft, 2,700 pounds lighter, was soaring upwards.

The electro-magnets had cut out, releasing the batteries. Houot and Willm had the satisfaction that their safety devices were working efficiently, but this seemed poor consolation for the enforced curtailment of their cruise over the ocean floor.

They rose through a multitude of phosphorescent lights—luminous fish in myriads.

Breaking the surface at 3.21 p.m., they opened the air-blast, and for a quarter of an hour the sea water ran steadily out of the float. When the air-lock was empty they raised the hatch, and went quickly up the ladder. Three turns of the hand-wheel released the hatch and they emerged into the open air, to find the *Élie Monnier* a few hundred feet away, and the *Tenace* making ready to take them in tow, while the *Beautemps Beaupré*, with its load of journalists, was bearing down on them. The F.N.R.S.3 had accomplished its sensational task successfully.

Despite the thickness of its walls it might well be described as a bubble—a man-made one which had penetrated the skin of this spinning bubble which we call our world.

How little we know of the world's seas may be appreciated when we realize that the descent of the F.R.N.S.3

was a mere "pin-prick" of exploration, so minute that it examined only a square mile or so at most of the 141 million square miles of the world's sea-beds. Yet even so limited an exploration can convince us that the sea is truly overwhelming—physically, because it covers seven-tenths of the earth, and mentally as we glimpse the wonderment and mystery concealed in its deeps, reflected from its surface, and expressed in the millions of living creatures which inhabit its shores.

CHAPTER II

ARE THERE OCEANS IN OUTER SPACE?

THE deeps of the world's oceans are easily accessible when compared with the appalling abysses which separate us from the stars, or even those which stretch between our world and the nearest planets in our solar system. *Proxima Centauri*, the nearest star, is so remote that light, travelling at 186,300 miles per second, takes over four years to reach us. Mars and Venus, the two nearest members of our sun's family, are very roughly 40 million miles away. Compared with such distances a journey down into the ocean deeps of a few miles seems a mere step.

Any kind of exploration of the 4,000 miles of solid earth or rock that separates us from the centre of the earth would indeed be a formidable task—perhaps even more impossible than a voyage across space to *Proxima Centauri*. The internal regions of the earth may forever remain unknown to us, save for anything we may learn of them by the use of seismographs and similar appliances.

But if these considerations give us an impression that the accumulation of knowledge regarding the world's oceans is a comparatively easy matter, we should pause to reflect that any voyage upward towards the planets or stars must be one through space, while a journey down into the ocean takes us through vast multitudes of living creatures—untold millions of them in every foot or so of sea water that we pass through.

Before we begin our imaginative voyage—across the

ocean's surface, along parts of its coastlines, and down into the deeps—we must have some conception of man's relation to the world's seas, and a mental picture of the oceans as compared with our world, and with the solar system.

Man is a creature dependent upon the earth (his natural habitat) for his daily life and substance. He depends upon air for the purification of his blood—and no artificial expedients can make him independent of it for long. He also depends upon fire for his existence—that mysterious phenomenon which is conditioned by the sun, directly and indirectly. But he is most intimately dependent on water, for his body is mainly composed of it. In fact, by a curious coincidence, the percentage of water in man's body roughly approximates to the seven-tenths preponderance of the world's water surface as compared with its land area.

Man's natural habitat, earth, is one across which fire and water wage incessant warfare. In this warfare the air is an instrument, or weapon used by the protagonists, rather than a field of action. Water—whether in the form of the world's oceans, or as rivers or streams, or merely in the form of torrential rains—attacks the earth, crumbling and eating away the world's coastlines, incessantly changing the shapes of countries and continents, and killing millions of humans through the centuries by wrecking man's ships and smashing his dwellings with devastating floods.

Fire retaliates by destroying man's dwellings and forests whenever he relaxes his watchfulness. Man enlists the aid of either of the protagonists as it suits him, but he is forever menaced by both, despite the paradoxical fact that they are his natural friends as well as enemies.

Man is curiously situated in relation to this incessant warfare. He lives upon a spinning globe, slightly flattened at the poles—a globe which has often been compared, quite appropriately as regards shape, with an ordinary

21

orange. But the comparison fails if we imagine the tiny irregularities on the skin of an orange as representing the mountains, valleys and ocean beds of our world. Even the smoothest-skinned orange would be too coarsely surfaced to represent them—an orange-sized ball with an apparently smooth surface would be a better representation.

The earth's diameter is nearly 8,000 miles. Compare it with the heights of the world's loftiest mountains, and the deepest depths of its oceans. Twenty mountain peaks are over 20,000 feet in height. Of these the highest is Everest—29,028 feet. One of the deepest spots in the oceans was discovered south-west of Guam in 1951 by the British survey ship *Challenger*—named after the famous oceanographic vessel that circled the globe in 1872–76. Known as the Challenger Depth, this is six and four-fifths miles down into the earth, and might seem to be more than a scarcely-visible prick in the skin of an orange. But even if we increase the Challenger Depth a little, calling it, for convenience's sake, seven miles, it is still less than a thousandth of the diameter of the earth.

There can be little doubt that human beings will one day descend to the deepest points in the world's oceans— probably exploring chasms many hundreds of feet deeper than those known to us at present. But enough exploration has already taken place to give us a rough idea of the downward limit of ocean penetration. We can accept seven miles as a reasonable figure. But the *average* depth of the world's oceans has been calculated at very considerably less than this: 14,200 feet, or roughly $2\frac{2}{3}$ miles. Some authorities make it somewhat less.

All man's normal activities take place within the twelve and a half miles range indicated: that is, in the superficial "thickness" lying between the top of Everest and the lowest depth in the ocean. The use of the word "normal" is essential in this age, for men occasionally pass upward, far above Everest, making their altitude records, such exploits being exceptions, however, to the normal life of man. And although the altitude figures in international aircraft records have crept up and up, from 38,419 feet in 1927 to the record height (as I write these words) of 100,000 feet attained by Major David G. Simons, in a manned freed balloon, of more than nineteen miles, in August 1957, yet the limit of man's physical penetration into the world's atmosphere probably still falls short of thirty miles.*

The clearest and most accurate conception of the three "elements", earth, air and sea, that we can possibly create is one which needs a pictorial representation of the world with a diameter of five feet. Any smaller scale makes it impossible to show the average depth of the oceans as a perceptible line. Many books which attempt to give pictorial representations of the earth, surrounded by its atmosphere and its oceans, are compelled to exaggerate the depth of the oceans for that reason.

If you can find a convenient surface—an appropriate one would be a smooth stretch of sand when you are next at the seaside—you can get a rough idea of the average depth of the world's oceans as compared with the earth itself by tracing a circle with a diameter of five feet. If the line you have drawn is not thicker than a fiftieth of an inch you will have some idea of the thinness of the film of water that covers our world. Yet film-like though it is compared with the diameter of our world, its depth is formidable for us, as we send down our bathyscaphes into it, and its volume is truly overwhelming.

For the total weight of the world's waters has been calculated as amounting to one and a half million million million tons, a figure which may perhaps be better appreciated if we realize that, shared among the 2,500 million human beings who constitute the present population of our world, it would give every man, woman and child 600 million tons of sea-water each.

*Even if we allow a margin for aircraft flights, details of which have not been officially released.

Statistics regarding the world's oceans abound in such paradoxes, even as the knowledge man has gained of them sparkles with countless facts, some of them so amazing that they seem miraculous.

The diagram on the following page should now be easily understood. It emphasizes in pictorial form the fact that the world is not "three parts water" as some people imagine, using loose terminology, but mainly *covered* with water, and that so superficially that we live upon a sphere which is almost entirely dry (almost completely waterless) when its bulk is compared with the film of water overwhelming its surface.

Because we are surface creatures we necessarily obtain a very distorted impression of the volume of the ocean as compared with the mass of the earth, and with our conception of the solar system itself.

We are microscopical life-forms in a planetary system which may seem vast to us as we circle our parent sun, but which is actually a minute speck compared with the Cosmos itself.

If the world were completely smooth it would be flooded to a depth of two miles, so that "dry land life" as we know it could not possibly exist upon it. Even now, if we consider the significance of the fact that the world's dry land has an average elevation above the surface of the sea of only 2,500 feet (a film of dry land so thin that it cannot possibly be represented by a line thin enough in our diagram) our position as dry land creatures is precarious.

A disturbance of sufficient severity in any of the ocean beds could raise the level of the world's waters that slight fraction, proportionately, which would result in a flooding of its entire land surface.

Fortunately for us the waves of the ocean scarcely rise above its average surface level. Yet the total volume of the waters resting on the world's sea beds is 324 million cubic miles—fourteen times as great as the volume of the

THE SOAP-BUBBLE SKIN

which we know as the world's oceans in relation to outer space

MILES

ABOVE
EXTREME
LIMIT OF
RAREFIED
ATMOSPHERE

NOT TO
SCALE

25,757 million miles: Nearest star (Proxima Centauri)
93 million miles: Mean distance of our sun
35 million miles: Mars at nearest
238,860 miles: Mean distance of the moon
4,000 miles: The Farside rocket

600 — Limit of extremely rarefied atmosphere

500

400

300 — Area of the Sputnik orbits

200

150 — Limit of dense atmosphere

100

— Limit of manned freed-balloon flight

19 — Mt. EVEREST

THE WORLD'S OCEANS

Average depth: 2⅔ miles

THE EARTH *(nearly 8,000 miles diameter)*
REPRESENTED ON THIS SCALE BY 5ft. CIRCLE.

25

SOLAR SAHARA

Compared with our world, the rest of our solar system (the sun and its other major planets) is almost waterless. Our world oceans, a mere film of water, comparatively, covering our planet, may be unique among the billions of solar systems in the known universe.

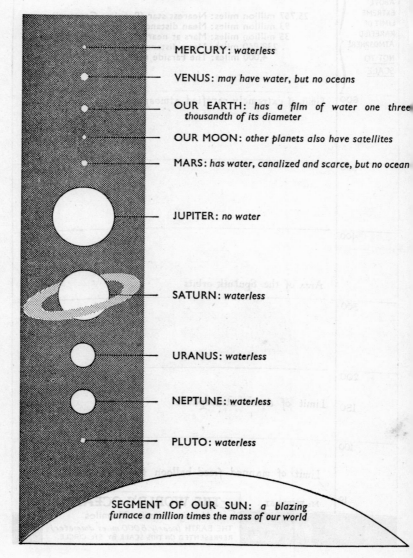

MERCURY: *waterless*

VENUS: *may have water, but no oceans*

OUR EARTH: *has a film of water one three thousandth of its diameter*

OUR MOON: *other planets also have satellites*

MARS: *has water, canalized and scarce, but no ocean*

JUPITER: *no water*

SATURN: *waterless*

URANUS: *waterless*

NEPTUNE: *waterless*

PLUTO: *waterless*

SEGMENT OF OUR SUN: *a blazing furnace a million times the mass of our world*

THE WORLD'S OCEANS

A water-film covering three-quarters of its surface

**WESTERN
HEMISPHERE**

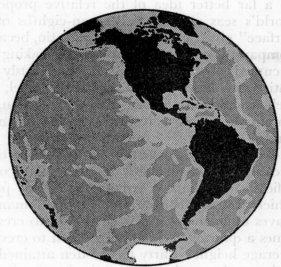

**EASTERN
HEMISPHERE**

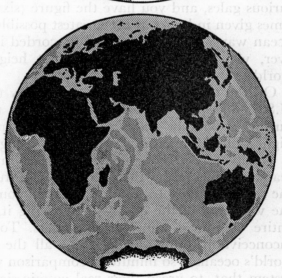

 Depths of 600 feet
and less

 Depths averaging
12,000 feet, includ-
ing the greatest
known deeps

dry land above sea level. Incidentally, these figures give us a far better idea of the relative proportions of the world's seas and lands. "Seven-eighths of the world's surface" gives us a seven-to-one ratio, because it merely compares the land and sea *surfaces*. Taking the sea as an occupied world or realm, and generously allowing the entire dry land surface above sea-level, vertically as well as horizontally, as man's habitation, the ocean's dominion is fourteen times greater than that of the land.

Compared with the enormous volume of the world's oceans, the waves of the sea are microscopically insignificant disturbances. Atlantic gales may produce waves which are truly enormous from any human viewpoint—waves often thirty feet from trough to crest, and sometimes a quarter of a mile from crest to crest. Double the average height—thirty feet—often attained by waves in furious gales, and you have the figure (sixty feet) sometimes given in books as the greatest possible height of an ocean wave. One was officially recorded in 1933, however, which actually exceeded that height. It is the world's record wave.

On the night of the 6th–7th February that year, the U.S.S. *Ramapo*, proceeding from Manila to San Diego during a 68-knot (78.3 m.p.h.) gale, measured that highest-of-all waves as 112 feet from trough to crest.

Terrifyingly high though such waves must appear to seamen menaced by them, any such disturbed area of the sea is actually tranquil and flat in comparison with the vast area of the ocean surrounding it. So with the entire volume of the world's waters. To us they are inconceivably immense. In truth all the water in the world's oceans is so minute in comparison with our solar system that, to grasp their real cosmic significance, we must see our sun and its nine major planets as a scorched and almost waterless desert.

Water in its various forms is at present our ally and

faithful servant—our sure defence against our solar system's greatest menace, subjected as it is to the incessant bombardment of the sun's rays. It is not an immediate threat, like the atomic bomb. But although the menace of the latter may well be cancelled out and removed by international understanding, there is nothing that mankind can do, ultimately, against the mightier menace of aridity, which must at last destroy all life on our world, even as it has (most probably) destroyed all life on some of the other planets.

Our sun has now lived approximately half its normal lifetime. Dr. Allan Sandage, astronomer of the Carnegie Institute (probably the world's greatest authority on this particular subject) has reached the conclusion that before our sun dies—doomed by the accumulated ashes of its fires—it must necessarily compensate for the change in its internal chemical composition by increasing its radius and luminosity. In other words it must expand and brighten if it is to remain stable. This increase in its size and in the power of its activity must, says Dr. Sandage, become far more pronounced and drastic when the sun has consumed twelve per cent of its fuel. Until now it has consumed about six per cent. In another six billion years the sun will appear as a dull red globe in the sky and will be burning out at a tremendous rate, declining in brightness until it will die out like an ember in a neglected fireplace. But long before this happens the temperature of the earth's surface must go up until the oceans have boiled away. Having reached a maximum temperature of 158 degrees Fahrenheit, the surface of the world will slowly cool again, but all life will have ceased and another arid and desolate planet will have been created in the Solar Sahara.

Whether fanciful or factual, such speculation on the future of our world can at least make us realize the vital preciousness of water. A quick survey of the solar system must inevitably deepen that realization.

Nearest to the sun, yet actually revolving 36 million miles from it, we see Mercury, with a diameter of 3,100 miles: a planet not much larger than our moon. Keeping one hemisphere forever turned towards the sun, Mercury has no day or night, and one side is therefore fiercely scorched, blazing with intense light and heat, while the other is forever shrouded in darkness. Although Schiaparelli and Antoniada imagined they saw clouds on Mercury's darker side, Dolfus, in 1953, dismissed the idea. It is now certain that water-droplets on Mercury would be as short-lived as snowflakes in a blast-furnace.

Moving away from the sun we come to Venus, with a diameter (7,575.4 miles) only slightly less than that of our own world. It is 67 million miles from the sun, and sometimes approaches to within 25 million miles of our earth. Astronomers have thought that the clouds which continually obscure its shining face might be composed of water-vapour and that parts of its surface might even be covered with water. But such probabilities have been shown in quite recent years to be very remote. Exhaustive investigation of the planet's atmosphere by means of the spectograph has shown neither water-vapour nor oxygen in detectable amounts. In fact recent researches have detected the presence of several hundred times as much carbon dioxide in its atmosphere as the amount present in our own.

That the surface of Venus is desert-like, and that high winds may easily account for clouds (which are not of water-vapour but of dust) seems as good a guess as any. Certainly there is no evidence whatever, as the result of investigations to date, of the existence of lakes on its surface, much less oceans.

Mars, on the other side of our world, outward from the sun and 142 million miles from it, is 35 million miles from our earth at its nearest. It certainly has water, but it seems certain that it has no oceans and that any water it possesses can only be present in limited quantities—in carefully conserved quantities if there are intelligent beings on Mars.

Those who argue for the existence of artificially constructed canals on Mars rightly point out that nowhere in Nature do we find long straight lines, and that only man produces such projects as railways and canals, which follow essentially straight lines for long distances. Hence, they argue, the markings on Mars must be caused by intelligent beings. Whatever may be the answer to the centuries-old problem of the existence of life on the red planet, we can be sure that water is very scarce there.

If the strange markings seen through our powerful telescopes are actually the irrigated regions bordering artificial water courses, then they certainly do not indicate the presence of large bodies of water like our own oceans. Some of the world's most efficient observers, using its most powerful telescopes, have failed to see the fine straight markings described in detail by Schiaparelli, Perrotin, Thollon, A. S. Williams, Lowell and others. But careful examination of the recorded evidence compels any impartial investigator to belief that the canals have been seen, so that there is at least a *prima facie* case for the existence of water in limited quantities on Mars— but not, in any sense, oceans as we know them.

Beyond Mars, keeping our backs to the sun, we see Jupiter, a huge giant out there in space, revolving in its orbit at a distance of 484 million miles from the sun, and nearly 400 million miles from our earth. It has a diameter over eleven times that of our own planet, and possesses a deep atmosphere, 17,000 miles thick, composed of methane and ammonia—dense and poisonous to life as we know it.

If Jupiter has any kind of ocean it is probably one of solid ice. Certainly not water ice, the frozen stuff which we know, but frozen ammonia or methane. Nor are its clouds water-vapour clouds, but vast misty masses of ammonia crystals.

31

All our human investigations fail to detect the presence of any water on the planet—not even pools of it. Jupiter definitely has no oceans.

Beyond Jupiter lie Saturn (with its amazing ring system), Uranus, Neptune and Pluto. We need not consider the three outermost planets in detail. Very little is known of them, and anything we do know suggests that conditions on them resemble those on Saturn—conditions quite waterless. The rings of Saturn may be composed of vast clouds of dust, or grains of sand, with larger bodies among them. The average density of Saturn is less than that of water.

There can be no oceans on the surfaces of the four outermost planets—most certainly none containing animal or plant life. Their enormous distances from the sun—the nearest of the four outermost planets is more than nine times farther out from the sun than our own planet—clearly indicate that they are waterless, frozen worlds.

We have found, in our rapid survey of the sun's nine major planets, that water only exists in any quantity in our own world.

In the light of all these facts, how infinitely precious is this film of water which covers our spinning globe! It may be that the ocean, with its hosts of living creatures, is absolutely unique, not merely in our solar system, but in the entire Cosmos, with its millions of millions of systems.

Earth, air and water—each designed to support multitudinous forms of life on our planet—are three distinct worlds. Of the three, water is by far the most densely populated. As we survey the surfaces, fringes and deeps of the ocean we become increasingly convinced that it constitutes a wonderland of singular beauty and fantasy. We go "through the looking-glass" of its sky-reflecting surface to find, in Alice's own words, that it gets "curiouser and curiouser".

CHAPTER III

SKIMMING THE SURFACE

THE ocean can again be divided into three inhabited areas or "living spaces". The highest of these consists of the surfaces of the seas, together with the atmosphere immediately above them. Below this "world" of surface creatures lies an area known to oceanographers as the Neritic Province. This consists of the shallower waters fringing the world's coasts—the area lying above the great continental shelves. Below this area and beyond the shelves lie the vast ocean basins, the abysses—teeming with living creatures known and unknown to us—comprising the Ocean Province.

But any survey of the oceans, surfaces, and the creatures which move upon them and often rise above them, must include the surfaces of the Ocean Province: the greatest of our oceanic sub-divisions and one which extends from the sea-beds right up to the wave-crests of the sea.

Among the larger and more active animals which inhabit the surface-waters of the Ocean Province are flying herrings, flying gurnards, flying squid, tunny fishes, dolphins, turtles, sharks, sun-fishes, sauries, horse-mackerel, salmon and whales. Some of these go down to great depths—others spend their lives near the surface. It might seem that whales and flying-fishes have little in common, yet they share a liking for spectacular leaps into the air. In this chapter we shall consider some of the marine creatures which live near the surface of the sea, move upon it, or are actually able to rise above it. These surface gymnasts include some of the most extraordinary creatures in the ocean.

Salmon—the Latin name *salmo* means "the leaper"—inhabit mostly the temperate and arctic zones of the world, and are found both in the salt seas and in fresh waters. The question has often been discussed whether the salmonids—so many of which live in the sea, yet resort to rivers for breeding purposes—were originally marine or fresh-water creatures. The balance of scientific opinion, however, is in favour of the marine theory, which is strongly supported by the fact that the overwhelming majority of the fishes in the sub-order of which the salmonids form part, inhabit the sea permanently.

Owing to fishery restrictions, salmon are no longer among the largest families of fishes, but (in the words of Dr. D. S. Jordan, one of the eminent ichthyologists of the last century) "in beauty, activity, gaminess, and quality as food, and even in size of individuals, different members of the group stand easily with the first among fishes".

Some of the species, especially the larger ones, are marine creatures, living and growing in the sea, and swimming to fresh waters to spawn. Others live in running brooks, occasionally travelling to inland fresh-water lakes or outward to salt waters. Others again are lake fishes, approaching the shore, or entering brooks in the spawning season, or at other times retiring to waters of considerable depth. Some kinds of salmon are voracious and venturesome, while others are modest and cautious and will not take the hook. Salmon are a comparatively recent development among fishes—none of them occur as fossils, unless it be among quite recent deposits. The fact that they have so quickly adapted themselves to live in both salt and fresh water is therefore little short of miraculous.

The Atlantic salmon feeds avidly on crustaceans, small shrimps and young crabs, and their eggs, while it remains in the sea or in brackish estuaries. As an adult, a little more than four years old, it enters a river and works its way towards the river's source. It has probably not been very far from the river where it was born, but there are striking exceptions to this. In fact the life of the salmon during the time it spends in the sea—at least one year and very often considerably longer—is still a mystery. We continue almost completely ignorant of what salmon do, and where they go in the sea. Yet salmon have been studied far more than most fish.

They normally swim at an average rate of eleven miles per hour. But experiments have been carried out which show that salmon can swim far faster than this, in fact that they hold the speed record for inland fish. Emerson Stringham, in the *American Naturalist*, showed that computations made on the basis of the height that a salmon leaps above water were proof that the fish can attain a velocity of over twenty-two miles an hour; while an English writer, Ernest Prothero, says: "No current is rapid enough to daunt it; it can dart along at thirty miles an hour, easily surmounting obstacles such as falls, by leaps of ten to fifteen feet." The truth probably lies between these estimates. Frank W. Lane, who has given exhaustive study to the speeds attained by living creatures of all kinds, gives the salmon a maximum speed of twenty-five miles an hour, timed with a stop-watch.

Wonderful migrations are made by Pacific salmon. The Chinook, or "king salmon", which is the largest of these (it has been known to weigh as much as a hundred pounds) may travel 1,000 miles up the Columbia river to its parent stream, or even farther up the Yukon river of Alaska. It recognizes its original home by some instinct unknown to us.

On their upward journeys into rivers salmon eat nothing, so that their stomachs shrink to negligible proportions. They enter the rivers in magnificent condition and fight their way up-stream with extraordinary persistence and force. Each male chooses his mate for the perilous journey, and he and his "wife" keep together all the way. The jaws of the male fishes develop fanged canines for fighting their rivals. So, faithful to each other and with the male fighting off any interfering rivals, the couples battle their way onward against swift currents, often tearing their flesh against sharp stones, climbing cataracts and leaping unbroken falls of considerable height.

The shrinking of their stomachs from the time they leave tide-water is accompanied by a narrowing of their throats. These remarkable changes are gradual, but they increase until all desire for food is gone, and any temptation to turn back to the rich feeding grounds of the salt waters vanishes. The great reserve of flesh and blood which they bring with them from the ocean enables them to keep their vital organs active until their strange mission up the fresh-water streams is accomplished.

This is one of the ocean's greatest mysteries. The fish face colossal hazards. They fight against the strong currents. They climb cataracts and are dashed back again and again—yet still they persist. As they ascend the American rivers, and those of other countries, they are caught by gill nets, fyke nets, pounds, weirs, seines, wheels, and other devices.

Before they enter the rivers they are fiercely attacked by seals and sea-lions, and many other natural enemies meet them on their way up-stream, apart from their greatest enemy, man, with his fishing rods and ingenious traps.

The force which drives them onward is the sexual instinct. But this fact deepens rather than lessens the mystery, for it does not explain why they have to go such long distances up-stream to the places where they were born to gratify it—nor how they remember the locations all their lives and are able to identify them again. We only know that they do return to their parent streams.

After their arrival, the female salmon pours out her eggs in vast quantities, and while this is happening the eggs are fertilized (outside the female's body) by the milt of the male, so that impregnation takes place immediately. The male then guards the impregnated eggs—which are unusually large compared with those of some other fishes—and fights off any other males who approach. The number of eggs deposited is enormous. It has been calculated that over 150 million salmon ova are annually deposited in the Scottish river Tay alone. Other fishes, birds and insect larvae devour quantities of the eggs, so that only a small proportion hatch out.

The young salmon lies coiled up in its egg, which it finally bursts in its struggle for freedom. It issues with a slender snout, semi-transparent and extremely delicate. Suspended under its belly is a conical bag—the "yolk-sac"—which contains the red yolk of the egg and oil globules. For about six weeks the maturing embryo takes no food save that which it obtains from this portable larder. During this period it hides in crevices among stones, and keeps up a perpetual fanning with its pectoral fin.

When the yolk-sac has gone the young salmon feeds greedily on small creatures and puts on a mottled coat which makes it resemble a young trout. At this stage it is usually known as a parr, or samlet, though in some places by the names pink, brandling or fingerling. Many anglers have argued that the parr is no salmon but a distinct species, but Mr. Shaw of Drumlanrig, between 1834 and 1836, made experiments on the Tay which have convinced naturalists for all time that the parr is nothing else than the young salmon.

The parr stage lasts until the fish assumes the silver mail of the smolt, and is ready to descend to the sea. It cannot do so until the change has taken place—a parr will die at once in salt water. But when it becomes a smolt, perhaps six inches in length, it develops an imperative hunger for the sea. It may go to the sea when a year old, or two or even three years old.

After two months in the sea the salmon has gained

37

several pounds in weight and is known as a grilse. From that stage onwards, and until the time comes when the salmon feels the urge to fight its way up-stream through the same river, it may or may not voyage out into the ocean wastes. Some certainly travel enormous distances. As recently as the autumn of 1955, a salmon tagged in Ross-shire eleven months earlier was recaptured off the coast of Greenland, having travelled 1,700 miles. This incident is regarded as one which affords an important clue to the problem—nevertheless the habits of the fish while it passes through the salt-water stage of its amazing existence still constitute one of the sea's most baffling mysteries.

The salmon's leaps over rapids may seem to be a kind of flight, but they are not flying fishes in any sense—their mighty jumps are empowered by initial propulsive efforts through the water, and not by any motion of their fins as wings.

But some fishes have appendages closely resembling wings, and use them with extreme rapidity as they travel through the air, although they manipulate them to maintain height rather than to propel themselves forward. Most flying fishes glide, rather than fly with "wing" motions. Frank W. Lane, in his *Nature Parade*,* describes how a flying-fish "flies". He says that the fish uses its abnormally large pectoral fins as supporting surfaces, while its initial impulse, which empowers the entire flight after it has caused the fish to leave the water, comes from a rapid "sculling movement" of the lower lobe of the caudal fin or tail. He gives the underwater speed as only thirty-five miles an hour, but this speed is fast compared with a shrimp's "speed"—a mile in four hours. Swimming creatures of the sea vary amazingly in their rates of progression. Between the lazy crawl through water of the shrimp and the flying-fish's flashing leap lie the bream's mile and a quarter an hour and the four

*Jarrolds (London) Ltd., 1946.

miles an hour amble of the octopus, which approximates to the walking speed of a man. These are of course speeds taken at random from the rising scale of fish progression.

The flying-fish's underwater speed is greatly exceeded when it takes to the air. In fact the common flying-fish of the larger variety (*Catalina*) holds the record for the fastest speed through the air authentically recorded, of any flying creature of the sea: fifty miles an hour in a favourable wind. This particular fish has been known to travel a quarter of a mile through the air before falling to the surface again—easily the record air distance travelled by any creature which rises from beneath the sea.

Considering that the best authorities agree that the fish is literally *shot* through the air by the "sculling movement" of its tail, what must be the enormous force of that initial propulsive effort? The speed attained by that terrific thrust of the fish's tail-muscles exceeds the speeds of such birds as the lapwing, the curlew and the starling which travel by wing propulsion. It is seven miles an hour faster than the fastest speed ever attained by a racehorse on land,* and equal to the speed of a charging lion.

Common to the sub-tropical trade-wind belts of the world, flying-fish often take to the air to escape the attacks of their enemies, such as bluefish, albacore, bonitos, tunas, swordfish and porpoises; but they also shoot into the air when disturbed by ships, and for other reasons unknown to us. Several authorities suggest that they sometimes do it for sheer joy of living. While in actual flight through the air they are often chased by birds—who probably resent the invasion of their own realm.

Of the two types of flying-fishes, the true flying-fish and the gurnards, the latter are the more curious. The gurnard is an armoured fish, for its large bony head has

---

*43 m.p.h., by the famous American racehorse, Man o' War, who on one occasion did the ¼ mile in 21 seconds.

hard keeled scales, two dorsal fins, and other peculiar characteristics, making it a grim, aggressive creature. Some have long barbels on their chins, making them look even more grotesque.

The flying gurnards are less numerous than the flying herrings (which are more closely allied to the gar-pike than the herring, despite their name), there being only three or four species of the former compared with nearly sixty of the latter, which are found in numerous shoals—often thousands in a shoal.

Flying-fish cannot turn or guide themselves in their flight, which is parabolic, like the flight of shells fired from guns—appropriately enough, for they resemble projectiles more nearly than do the majority of fishes. It would be wrong to think of them as jet-propelled. That word can be more appropriately applied to animals which propel themselves through the water by exhaling jets. Of about 300 species of swift-travelling fish which have been examined, 270 species possessed gill-clefts at the right positions, potentially, for efficient jet-propulsion.

All the fast-swimming types of fish in the ocean are streamlined, and have full control of their water-ejection systems, so that they can increase or decrease speed at will and make efficient turns. Many fish have had an "induced stream-line system", using jet-propulsion in highly efficient ways.

Although the flying-fish holds the record for the fastest speed *through the air* of any creature normally living in the sea, it is by no means the fastest fish *in the sea*. The sail-fish has that distinction. Although it is not a true swordfish it is closely related—it differs in having teeth, scales, ventral fins of a few rays, and a very large dorsal fin. The latter may give it the advantage in speed over the true swordfish of a few miles an hour.

The sword of a swordfish, although solid and as hard as ivory, is not so strong that it could be forced through the hulls of wooden ships unless the speed at the moment of impact was at least sixty miles an hour. There are instances of such powerful penetration that the sword of the fish has been forced through twenty inches or more of hard wood sheathed with copper. Such instances clearly indicate an enormous speed at the moment of impact, so that (considering the nature of the "sword" and the depths of penetration) sixty miles an hour is evidently no exaggeration.

The shape of the sail-fish's body is admirably adapted for its high-speed, torpedo-like actions. Its sword is not as long as that of the true swordfish, but the fish itself reaches a total length of over six feet, has a stream-lined flexible body, sloping back to its great deeply-forked tail: a body covered with elongated "scutes", or horny plates. The huge dorsal fin, deeply notched, simulates the appearance of a ship under sail as it appears above the water.

Swordfish may be classified among surface creatures of the sea, and only the fact that its occasional leaps into the air are not prolonged into gliding flights (for which it is not naturally adapted) prevents some of its species from challenging the flying-fish's above-water record. But the sail-fish's *under-water* record of seventy miles an hour (vouched for by unimpeachable authorities) makes the flying-fish's *over-water* record of fifty miles an hour seem insignificant, when the resistances of the media are compared. To fully appreciate the underwater speed of the sail-fish, and the extraordinary efficiency of its stream-lined structure, one should compare the speeds attainable by man's inventions: the submarine and the aeroplane. Seventy miles per hour would be an extraordinary speed for a submarine—yet the sail-fish is not a mechanism but a living creature.

Whatever creatures may be found on the ocean floors —or may remain to be discovered—one cannot imagine that any will be more fantastic than those we are now examining on the surface of the world's seas—yet space forbids mention of more than a few of the numerous varieties which live in that vast area where waves and atmosphere meet.

Swordfishes and their near relatives might be likened to torpedoes, but any such comparison, however picturesque, would be inadequate. It is in fact difficult to conceive how such macabre creatures could possibly have evolved by any of the processes usually associated with nature. Superficially considered, the fearsome projection from the swordfish's head may seem to be a weapon of defence, but in the long process of evolution, and before it became efficient, the fishes possessing it would surely have been at a serious disadvantage in the struggle for survival. And why should living torpedoes survive, anyway? The devastating effect of the sixty miles an hour impact of a swordfish on the hull of a wooden vessel could only be equalled by man if he used some kind of explosive, a super-ram in the form of another vessel striking the hull at high speed, or a long series of blows with a heavy hammer. The force involved seems wasted when applied to smaller fish than the swordfish itself (which the creature depends upon for food) yet it is ridiculous to assume that swordfishes developed their powerful weapons to attack ships, long before ships existed!

Most of the fast-swimming fish use principles applied in man's most modern submarines. For instance, numbers of them have a sac-like chamber (the swim-bladder) which contains gas. When the fish sinks into lower depths, gas is extracted: when it rises towards the surface, gas is pumped into the swim-bladder. The fish can therefore rise or sink or remain at any depths it chooses.

All man's inventions are foreshadowed in lower creatures in one form or another. The ant uses a comb, the earwig uses tweezers, the aphis has a vacuum-cleaner, the ichneumon-fly its own drill, the snail its file. But apart from land animals and insects, and creatures of the air (all of which were using man's "inventions" in principle long before he appeared on the earth) we could possibly find all man's ideas and devices, in embryo, in the ocean.

There are about forty species of the gurnard, which is one of the most extraordinary fishes in the sea. We are considering it among surface fish, but most of the gurnards live near the bottom, feeding on crustaceans, molluscs and small fishes.

The head of a gurnard is mailed and cuirassed, while the gill-cover and shoulder-bones are covered with spines having trenchant blades which give the fish its hideous appearance, and account for some of its names: such as sea-devil, sea-scorpion and sea-frog. Yet its glorious colours—as beautiful as those of any fish in the sea—have given the gurnard other names, less opprobrious, such as sea-robin. The sapphirine gurnard, for instance, is so named from the exquisite blue of its pectoral fins.

The most marked peculiarity of the genus is the presence of three freely-moving finger-like rays in front of the pectorals. These are furnished with elaborate nerve-systems, and are organs of both locomotion and touch. In the seas around Britain the commonest species is the grey gurnard. The flying gurnard is somewhat similar to this, but differs in having the fin-rays of the pectorals connected by membranes or "webs", by which it is enabled to support itself in the air.

The flying gurnard can walk on land, swim in the sea, and fly in the air, so that it resembles a tank, submarine and seaplane, all in one.

Having given the gurnard so many extraordinary qualities, its range of glorious colourings being not the least of them, it almost seems that Nature decided to "go the whole hog" and looked around for some other queer faculty to bestow upon it, and chose (of all things) the faculty of "speech", enabling the creature to make hog-

43

like grunts! For gurnards do emit such sounds, and boatmen who have heard them out at sea have often described them as not merely hog-like but uncannily human. Some authorities say that the grunts are emitted only when the fish are handled, and that they are caused by air escaping from the air-bladders. But there is some evidence that the gurnard often makes the noise when swimming.

One authority suggests that the sudden little bellow, which sounds alarming even to human ears, has some purpose in enabling the gurnard to frighten away its foes. This theory implies that many creatures of the sea have hearing—an idea which was once thought untenable, but is now gaining a measure of acceptance. The noises made by one species of gurnard has gained it, locally, the name of "piper".

The flying squid is another extraordinary creature among those which shoot themselves into the air, or leap upward from the waves. Its body is long, cylindrical, and pointed towards the rear end, and it has two triangular fins which it uses to project itself from the water—sometimes to such a height that it will fall to a ship's deck, a circumstance which has given the fish the name among sailors of "sea-arrow". The flying squid is one species of a genus of decapod (ten-legged) cephalopods. Like other cephalopods it swims by ejecting water forcibly from its mantle or gill cavities—jet-propulsion again.

Flying squid are included among those cephalopods which have the cornea of the eye open, so that sea water is in contact with the lens. The internal shell, or "pen", of the flying squid is a very interesting structure. It has three diverging rays and a hollow conical appendage. The species vary in length from one to four feet, yet to this family belong the giant squids which inhabit the arctic and sub-arctic seas, and are occasionally stranded on the shores of Norway and Greenland. All the species are fish-eaters.

"In attacking the mackerel," says Verrill, "they suddenly dart *backward* among the fish with the velocity of an arrow." The name "sea-arrow" may therefore have a dual origin—it may have been bestowed on the flying squid by fishermen who have known of its method of attacking mackerel or other fish, apart from the use of the name by mariners who have seen "sea-arrows" fall on to the decks of their ships.

The flying squid shows uncanny skill in attacking mackerel and other fish. Once among them it will suddenly turn obliquely to the left or right, seize a fish, and instantly kill it by biting it in the back of the neck with its sharp beak. This is an amazingly efficient operation, and is performed with such rapidity that it reminds us of the practice of the spider, which cuts a nerve of its victim so quickly and skilfully that it is not killed but paralysed: the spider needing the helpless victim alive and with its blood circulating, for its larder.

Tarpon are acrobatic fish which grow to a length of seven feet or more, and may weigh anything up to 350 pounds. Any over a mere twenty-five or thirty pounds can tow a spearman and his boat with ease.

The fish has a peculiar modification of its dorsal fin: the last ray is drawn out in a whip-like filament, which seems to aid the tarpon in its sensational leaps. Before jumping, the fish whips this filament to the side of its body and clamps it there: an action which has the effect of holding the dorsal fin rigidly at an angle. This angle, remarkably enough, is *prearranged* by the fish in accordance with the course of its leap—to left or right as the case might be. A few authorities doubt the truth of this prearranged fixation of the dorsal fin, but all seem to agree that the "whip" is used in some way in relation to the leap, and if it is not used to hold the fin rigid there seems to be no purpose in it as an appendage, while the creature's movement before leaping remains mysterious.

Tarpon are provided with very large gills by means of

which they extract the enormous amount of oxygen required for their tremendous exertions. They have been known to leap as high as eighteen feet into the air, across a distance of thirty feet.

The finest tarpon-fishing in the world is carried on near the coasts of Florida, where spearmen in some areas are not allowed to shoot the fish. In other areas, fierce struggles often take place if the tarpon is not killed with the first shot, for tarpon will fight to the death, even though badly wounded. Yet despite the incessant warfare carried on against them by man they are surprisingly tame if not attacked.

In contrast with the tarpon, the marine sunfish is a lazy creature, and prefers to move slowly about on the surface. It is often seen sleeping on the sea, quite motionless, or perhaps turning round and round like a wheel. It is almost circular in form, as its name implies: the posterior part of its body looks as though a part of the fish had been cut squarely off and the tail replaced on the line of severance. Some naturalists say that this actually happens in its early development: that it loses part of its posterior and grows a new tail afterwards.

The gills of the sunfish are arranged in comb-like fringes. The fish may attain a length of four or five feet, and a weight of several thousand pounds. While floating and slowly revolving on the sea, the sunfish keeps its eyes just above the surface, so that it surveys the entire horizon as it makes one revolution.

Among the great game fishes of the seas the tunny is king—a monarch who survives and reigns despite the determined attacks on his kingdom by sportsmen of many nations. He is a royal and magnificent fish—in size, courage, fighting skill, and in his kingly contribution to the food of mankind. Immense numbers enter the Mediterranean by the Straits of Gibraltar in May and June, and immediately divide: one royal cortège following the shores of Europe and the other those of Africa, in search of places to deposit their spawn. But the tunny is found in all warm seas. It is one of the largest fishes of the mackerel family, sometimes attaining a length of ten feet and a weight of a thousand pounds.

Tuna-fishing—the tunny of the Pacific coast bearing the specific name of "tuna"—has been a fashionable sport for many years off the coasts of southern California and elsewhere, but fishing for tunny has actually been carried on since the days of the Phoenicians. Immense numbers have been caught through the centuries off the Spanish coast and in the Sea of Marmora, but in recent years the main areas of tunny-fishing have moved elsewhere, to the north coast of Sicily and other places.

The tunny had the honour, over one hundred years ago, of being the fish which led John Davy (brother of the eminent Sir Humphrey Davy) to a discovery which provided an exception to the time-honoured division of all vertebrate animals into warm-blooded and cold-blooded. John Davy examined the tunny and found that its blood-temperature could be considerably higher than that of the surrounding water. Until then it was assumed that all fish were cold-blooded.

The variations and movements of tunny and albacores were given royal attention when King Carlos of Portugal (1889–1908) studied the fish for many years, and finally wrote and published a compendious monograph on the subject, illustrated by remarkable charts and figures: a study of the king of surface fishes by a monarch who was anything but superficial in his researches. His political activities were not so successful as his labours in natural history. With his eldest son, Louis, he was assassinated in the streets of Lisbon.

It is an amazing fact regarding many surface fishes that the energy which drives even the largest of them (and even the energy which empowers that monstrous mammal the baleen whale) comes mainly from planktonic food, most of which consists of tiny organisms.

The word "plankton" does not merely mean "wandering", as it is usually translated, for the word has a distinctly passive sense, suggesting "that which is made to wander and drift". It therefore does not merely define the tiny creatures which form its greatest bulk, but all those creatures of the sea which float and drift with its tides and ocean currents (the animals and plants which are *passively* carried about) in contrast to whales and fish which swim and move at will through the waters. This means that the babies of all kinds of fish must be classed as plankton, if they are small enough to be borne helplessly along by the sea.

Tunny fishes consume large quantities of plankton, being quite indiscriminate regarding the nature of it, while flying-fishes also consume countless millions of planktonic creatures, particularly *Copepoda*.

These copepods constitute the large order of minute crustaceans (found in both salt and fresh water) which, by their abundance, provide food for all kinds of larger sea creatures. In typical copepods (the name means "oar-feet") the body is distinctly segmented, the abdomen is limbless, and the thorax bears four or five pairs of branched appendages. All of the tiny creatures are one-eyed. The appendages are truly oars rather than feet, for they are used for "rowing" by free-swimming copepods, but they can also be used to throw the creatures into the air with a kind of kicking action, resulting in multitudes of them falling to the surface again like rain.

Apart from the free-swimmers, which people the sea in vast numbers defying computation, many forms are parasitic, and these are usually larger than the free-swimming kind. One of these larger forms is the *Pennella*, a parasite on the whale, sometimes exceeding a foot in length. Many of these parasitical copepods will attack any host, but some specialize in fastening on to one kind of animal.

A curious feature of the parasitic copepods is that the male is often a mere pygmy attached to the female. He may in fact be as tiny compared with her as she is compared with the animal upon which she preys. Their "attachment" is a fantastic instance of the "little-fleas-have-lesser-fleas-and-so-on" principle in nature.

Free-swimming copepods, making up the greater part of planktonic life, are (despite the ugly habits of their parasitic relatives) among the most beautiful creatures in the sea. Their feathered antennae often exceed in length the dimensions of their bodies, and their lovely tail extensions have been compared with peacock's feathers. In some of these crustaceans an intense scarlet will merge into a brilliant blue, while others have different colour effects—many rivalling the rainbow in harmony and brilliance.

Copepods and other small sea organisms are filtered out of the flying-fish's inflowing respiratory stream by a series of fine "rakers" set on its gill arches. So with numerous other creatures which consume quantities of plankton—filters of all kinds are used to retain the essential food and strain off the water.

Even the massive ocean sunfish, which grows to as much as a ton in weight, feeds on small creatures like jellyfish and tiny crustaceans, with masses of other kinds of plankton, as it drifts lazily on the surface. In the North Atlantic the sunfish also consumes millions of the leaf-like larvae of certain eels, but always its staple diet is plankton.

Curiously enough, there is a tendency among the largest sea mammals and fishes to live on herbivorous planktonic animals (the "vegetarians" in the plankton), which means that they come as close as they can to an assimilation of "living energy". The vegetable plankton is the start of the various food-chains in the ocean and it seems to give the creatures who are the greatest consumers of it enormous power. Marine turtles, for

49

instance, some of which get their energy from consuming large quantities of planktonic creatures, can weigh over 400 pounds, and have been known to drag an eighteen-foot sailing boat for two or three miles.

Numerous living species of Chelonians (turtles and tortoises) are known. The limbs of a Chelonian may be either of two types—limbs, with free toes, for walking, in the land tortoises, or flattened paddles for propelling themselves through the water in the turtles. Some aquatic forms have additional respiratory organs.

Globe-fishes are the hedgehogs of the ocean surfaces. They are found on all the warmer coasts of the world, particularly within the tropics, and their extraordinary characteristics have earned them such picturesque names as "puffers", "swell-fish", "bellows-fish", and "rabbit-fishes"—the latter because of their rodent-like teeth. Globe-fishes are oval, spinose, small-finned fishes, which nibble barnacles and crunch other small crustaceans and molluscs found along the world's warmer coasts.

Looking ordinary enough when deflated, the globe-fish changes its appearance in a remarkable manner when danger threatens. It immediately sucks air or water into a large bladder-like membrane covering its abdomen until the fish becomes as round as a football, while its sharp spines arise from their normal position and stand up as stiffly as soldiers on parade with fixed bayonets. It has changed from what may have seemed a tempting morsel to one of its enemies to a most disagreeable mouthful, so that one can imagine a fish many times the size of the inflated globe-fish turning away and seeking a snack elsewhere. Yet sometimes a shark or other monster of the deep may swallow one.

If this happens the globe-fish takes a terrible revenge for the indignity. Having teeth as sharp as a rat's, and a beak as formidable as a parrot's, it bites its way to freedom through its enemy's stomach. There are stories of eels which have escaped to freedom in a similar manner, from the stomachs of herons and other creatures which have swallowed them.

Some tropical "puffers" are a foot long, but the fishy footballs most frequently seen are much smaller, including those which sometimes become comical additions to aquaria. The flesh of puffers is poor, and in some cases poisonous: as though they had become not merely assassins but Borgias in their determination to avoid being peacefully digested.

When fully puffed out, globe-fish turn over and float upside-down, carried here and there by the waves in nonchalant "touch me if you dare" attitudes.

The trigger-fish is seldom referred to in popular books on the sea, but is well worth examination. It has eight or ten genera and about one hundred species, all of which inhabit warm seas. A single species, however, wanders northward on the Atlantic coast as far as Cape Cod. It is a rather handsome fish, encased in heavy scales like a knight in armour, and has three stout dorsal spines or rays. When the dorsal fin is raised (it is very thick and strong) it holds its elevated position and cannot be pressed down. It has "locked" itself in its extended attitude. But if the *second* ray is depressed (or pulled, as a trigger is pulled) the first ray instantly falls flat—released as the hammer of a gun is released when the gun is fired.

Closely related to the trigger-fish is the file-fish, or fool-fish. The former name has been given the creature because of its rough and prickly skin, which is so abrasive that it can easily take the skin from a man's hand if the creature is carelessly handled. The latter name derives from the fish's large, expressionless, staring eyes, which give it a vacant, idiotic expression.

Despite their coarse skins and vacuous, foolish expressions, file-fishes are often most beautifully tinted. They have jaws of enormous strength, and can perform curious tricks with them. They can bite off chunks of coral which would blunt an ordinary chisel, crunching the stuff in their jaws as though it were pieces of candy. They can even crack the tough shells of oysters and devour the contents.

The file-fish is truly a clown, for he takes part in an extraordinary series of happenings, as though he were one of a group of comedians scoring off each other in a stage turn. For the file-fish preys on the oyster, but the game doesn't stop there—the ray preys on the file-fish, so that there is a kind of predatory merry-go-round. A certain thread-like parasite plays its own part as one of the actors in this "crazy gang". It passes the first phase of its existence in the body of the file-fish. Along comes a ray and devours the file-fish so that the thread-like parasite passes into the body of the ray. There it enters its next phase of existence and lays its eggs. When these little parasites hatch out they pour out from the body of the ray and enter the open shells of oysters, where they really begin their brief lives. The sensitive oyster protects itself against these unwelcome parasites. The irritation created by their presence causes the oyster to pour out the smooth, shining, iridescent substance which we call "nacre".

Of course any foreign body in the oyster may produce such irritation, but we are considering the life-cycle of a parasite which has just left the body of a ray in considerable numbers. The little worm pays a terrible price for its temerity in trespassing into the oyster's sanctuary—it is literally buried alive in the nacre as it hardens around it, and becomes a pearl. Some of the most costly pearls which adorn the throats of lovely women are the tombs of long-dead parasites.

Dolphins are not fishes, but mammals. They are often confused with porpoises, in fact one popular encyclopaedia says: "more commonly called porpoises". But the nose of a porpoise is a blunt, rounded snout, and is not produced into a "beak", as in the dolphin's case. Dolphins are found in abundance in all seas, while some species are inhabitants of large rivers, such as the Amazon.

The food of these animals is chiefly fish, and the dolphin's long and narrow "beak" is admirably adapted for this purpose as a weapon of offence. The muscular power of the dolphin is enormous. It has been calculated from its resistance to a towing-line that its muscles are capable of generating energy at least seven times greater than the muscles of other mammals.

The common dolphin usually measures from six to eight feet in length, tapering from the centre (where its dorsal fin rises to a height of about ten inches) to both extremities. The "beak" is about six inches long, and the mouth is armed with sharp, curved teeth—about forty or fifty on each side of its jaw. The ear aperture is extremely small, the eyes are of moderate size, and the "blow-hole" through which the creature breathes is crescent-shaped.

Dolphins occur in all seas, and feed mainly on fish, but they will eat lower creatures such as molluscs and crustaceans. They are greedy eaters and will on occasion consume cuttle-fish. The mother dolphin bears one baby (or very rarely, two) at a time, and she watches over her infant, or infants, with extraordinary care, even when they have grown to a considerable size. Her milk is rich and abundant, and she suckles her progeny with all the tenderness of a human mother, floating in a slightly sidelong position while doing so.

Calculated from the known speed of vessels, dolphins and porpoises travel at anything up to thirty-seven miles an hour. Dolphins, being the speedier of the two, may even exceed this speed on rare occasions. Dolphins have been watched by the crews of destroyers, doing over thirty knots—zigzagging from side to side in front of the vessels.

Dolphins and porpoises exhibit such amazing agility

that they might well be called the acrobats of the ocean's surface. They live in herds or "schools", and are often seen by ocean voyagers playing around the vessels as though they were "showing off" to the passengers. They will leap in graceful curves into the air, emerging and descending into the sea rhythmically, creating tracks of foam. Then they will reappear, displaying their slender back-fins before plunging below the water again, to rise from the surface again, almost before one has missed them, on the other side of the ship.

One member of the dolphin family, the blackfish (not to be confused with fishes of other families given the same name) travels in herds in which one fish acts as a leader or pilot. Hunters of the blackfish use this habit of the fish to their advantage, concentrating on the leader and knowing that wherever it goes the others will surely follow, with the result that numbers of the fish are captured because of their blind faith in their leaders.

Mariners of all ages have told stories of the amazing leaps and whimsical tricks of dolphins and porpoises, so that many fables and superstitions have developed about them. The structure of a dolphin's ear renders its sense of hearing very acute, and extended observations have led some authorities to the conclusion that the animal can appreciate musical sounds and is strangely attracted by them. It has a peculiar lowing cry, almost like the mooing of a cow. It is one of the most curious sounds uttered by those creatures of the sea which are able to give vocal expression to their feelings.

The most remarkable genus of the porpoise tribe, the narwhal or sea-unicorn, is the subject of many sea stories and superstitions. It inhabits the Arctic Ocean, and is remarkable for the possession of a very long, spirally-grooved tusk, which, in a narwhal twelve feet long, may measure as much as eight feet in length: two-thirds the entire length of the creature's body. This tusk is one of the most grotesque appendages possessed by any of the fantastic animals which frolic upon, skim over or leap from the ocean's surface. Composed of ivory, without enamel, it has a central cavity reaching almost to the apex, and the spiral grooves and ridges upon it run in a sinistral (turning from right to left) direction.

This massive, formidable and in many ways frightening weapon is developed only in the male narwhal, and (with very rare exceptions) only on the left side of its jaw. If it ever happens that a tusk develops on the right side of the jaw it never achieves the size of the huge one on the left of the jaw, but becomes one of a pair of approximately equal length. No case has ever been known of the development of a full-sized right-hand tusk, in association with a smaller left-hand one. In females neither tusk is visible. All other teeth are completely lacking in the male narwhal: all the ivory is used up in its two tusks, with the left-hand one monopolizing by far the greater amount of it. The enormous tusk is a secondary sexual characteristic of the narwhal—like the antlers of a stag, or the spurs and comb of a cock.

It has been suggested that the narwhal uses its huge, lop-sided, cumbersome instrument to break ice, and also to transfix its prey—but these suggestions have never been confirmed. For the ice-breaking theory has never been justified by any sight of a narwhal using its huge tusk in such a fashion, while the fact that the creature feeds on cuttle-fishes, small fishes and crustaceans disposes of the second suggestion, for the tusk would appear to be valueless as an instrument for attacking its victims or assimilating them.

Some authorities say that the males do battle with their tusks. William Scoresby and his son (of the same forename), the famous Arctic explorers, described the narwhal as a sportive rather than an aggressive creature, and said that the males were "extremely playful, frequently elevating their horns and crossing them with each other as in fencing".

The narwhal has never been known to charge and pierce the hulls of ships with his mighty weapon, as the swordfish does, although the narwhal's tusk might seem to be as well-adapted to the purpose. When first introduced into Europe as trophies, the tusks of narwhals were accepted as the horns of mythical unicorns, and as proof of the existence of such creatures. For a considerable time they were highly prized as talismans, and for their supposed medicinal qualities.

It is probable that more "magic" has accumulated around the sea-unicorn's tusk than around the appendage of any other animal of land or sea. Queen Elizabeth I was graciously pleased and delighted to accept a narwhal's tusk from Sir Martin Frobisher on his return from a valiant though vain dash into the Arctic regions. That it was apparently the only trophy he brought back seemed to make it all the more precious as a souvenir of that unsuccessful voyage.

We have examined only a few of the wonderful creatures which perform their antics on the sea's surface. The entire surfaces of the vast oceans, and of the world's lakes, rivers and streams, are alive with fishes, birds and insects in continuous motion: millions upon millions of living creatures whose lives and habits are curiously inter-related, and whose combined activities contribute to the mysterious progress of mankind itself.

Despite the nose-protrusions of sharks into the atmosphere, and the occasional cavortings of whales above the waves of the sea, such creatures are really underwater ones, and cannot be done justice to among surface creatures. They will receive special attention in later chapters, as will planktonic creatures—at the other extreme in size—when we go down into the deeps of the oceans, and (as far as we can) into the knowledge that has accumulated about such life-forms through the ages.

By far the larger proportion of such knowledge, however, is concerned with fish and other creatures which come to the surfaces of the world's seas, with the innumerable forms of life which inhabit the world's coastlines, and with the natural conditions which affect such surfaces and fringes.

Among the natural forces which create the conditions governing not merely the surfaces and fringes of the oceans, but also the conditions obtaining for a considerable distance downward into the deeps, so that they affect the life-forms and habits of myriads of sea creatures, are the winds of the world: those invisible currents of air, sometimes gentle and life-giving and at other times horrific in their destructive fury, which have pursued their complicated movements over the earth's surface ceaselessly and uncontrollably from the beginning of time.

CHAPTER IV

THE WINDS

FROM the dawn of human history until as recently as the middle of the nineteenth century, when old witches in Norway used to sell parcels of wind to superstitious sailors to prevent their ships becoming becalmed, the winds of the world have stirred the imaginations of men, and have breathed fables and superstitions regarding themselves in their ears.

Meteorology as an exact science treating of the motions and phenomena of the atmosphere begins with Hippocrates, the Greek physician, who in the fifth century B.C. wrote a work on *Airs, Waters and Places*; but speculation as to the physical causes of atmospheric changes began a century later, when Aristotle's *Meteorologica* appeared: it became the text-book of physical science for centuries afterwards, right up to the Middle Ages and the Renaissance. Only gradually, however, did meteorology become a specialized science. For more than a thousand years the men who contributed to the study of the world's winds, waves, whirlpools and other meteorological phenomena were not necessarily scientists. Valuable though their contributions were, they were men of widely diversified occupations, from chemists and mathematicians to lawyers and politicians. There were, of course, astronomers and seafaring men among them—men likely to be specially interested in meteorological conditions—but some of the most noted names are those of men whose occupations were in no way connected with meteorology. Pliny the Elder, whose *Historia Naturalis* is

an encyclopaedia of natural science, was a Roman pro-
curator and military leader. William Dampier, who
wrote "A Discourse on Winds" (1699) and made invaluable contributions to meteorology, was a notorious
buccaneer. John Dalton's *Meteorological Observations*
(1793), in which he maintained the electrical origin of
the aurorae, was published while he was a schoolmaster.
But the status of the meteorologist has undergone radical
changes during the last hundred years—the study of
wind and weather conditions demands the full-time
attention of numerous scientific experts.

The atmosphere which enfolds our earth is an invisible
sea which is constantly in motion. Forever striving to
attain a state of absolute rest and tranquillity, it is continually being disturbed and "moved on" by the torrential, daily-renewed stream of solar energy which pours
upon the earth from the sun.

It is fortunate for us that no area of the atmosphere,
however limited, is absolutely at rest for long, for stagnant air over our heads and around us would soon
become foul and poisonous. So the sun keeps the world's
air in constant motion, distributing the moisture that
makes life possible; carrying dust (necessary to the
formation of rain) up to the cloud regions; spreading
seeds of all kinds; bearing away the smoke of our cities,
and other poisonous exhalations including the breath of
man himself; and so (in these and many other ways)
purifying the atmosphere and directing it to the advantage of living creatures. Although solar energy is the
primary cause of wind motion there are many other
factors which influence the direction and force of the
winds. The atmosphere is held to the earth by gravity,
but this does not interfere with the fluidity or elasticity
of the air, nor with the effects of any pressures acting at
points within it, so that all parts of the atmosphere have
perfect freedom in their inter-relationships. If the entire
atmosphere were left undisturbed within itself it would

59

be carried round by the earth's spinning motion as though it were a solid shell. But it is in a state of turbulent motion everywhere as the result of the complicated interplay of several forces.

Most powerful of these is the sun's energy. Other forces acting upon the atmosphere and supplementing the sun's power are the gravitational "pulls" of the moon and the sun (although the latter influence is slight); the centrifugal (or "throwing off") effect of the earth's rotation; and the ascending and descending movements caused by the natural law that heated air rises while chilled air falls through the surrounding atmosphere. These up-and-down movements contribute very largely to the horizontal ones; for wherever the air ascends or descends other currents rush in laterally to replace the rising or falling columns.

As the surfaces of the earth and sea are heated by the sun's energy, air rises from them which carries water-vapour from the moister areas of the land, or from the seas, rivers and streams, and this water-vapour rises until it reaches colder zones, where it is chilled and forms clouds. On the other hand, wherever excess volumes of air may have piled up, or where the air currents may have cooled and therefore become heavier, masses of air may descend towards the earth's surfaces, again causing lateral winds. Such falling masses of air grow warmer by compression, and as they absorb more water-vapour the clouds tend to dissipate as they are affected by them, usually causing clearer skies. Rising and converging (low pressure) air currents are therefore accompanied by cloud-accumulation and rain, while descending and diverging (high pressure) currents are associated with lack of rain and cloud-dissipation.

The atmosphere is an invisible "ocean", and has its waves and tides. The atmospheric tides are of two kinds. One kind is due to the attraction of the sun and moon, and is therefore similar to the oceanic tides. But this tidal effect is slight, and affects the atmosphere as a whole. Its maximum effect on a column of mercury is only a hundred and thirtieth of an inch. But the other kind of atmospheric tide is a major influence in the world's atmosphere. It is a "heat tide" which follows the sun in its apparent circling of the earth, and is an elevation or crest of air along a meridional line, which moves steadily around the earth. As with the twice-daily oceanic tides, this "heat tidal wave" is related to a "cool tidal wave" on the opposite side of the earth.

These tidal waves, one kind gravitational and insignificant and the other kind caused by the sun's heat and affecting the atmosphere powerfully, are periodic. They merge with, or are affected by, wind modifications caused by irregularities in the world's land surfaces, so that the processes involved in the movements of the winds are, in detail, infinitely complex. The entire atmosphere is continually in motion, like the sea itself, as air currents, moving in every conceivable direction, struggle for ascendancy or battle for "right of way".

A curious phenomenon of air motion is called the Coriolis effect, after Gaspard G. de Coriolis (1792–1843), the eminent French mathematician who first investigated it. Any wind flowing "downhill" in the northern hemisphere tries to turn in an anti-clockwise direction, across the isobars, moving towards the nearest "valley" of low pressure available. But a new factor enters—one which remained obscure and perplexing until Coriolis explained it. The earth's surface in our northern hemisphere is steadily turning in an anti-clockwise direction— leftward around the pole. But the air above the earth's surface (being relatively free) tends to move straight onwards, urged by inertia, and this movement of the air, seen from *beneath* it, appears to us to be clockwise, because we, as observers, are on the earth's leftward turning surface.

As we contemplate the extreme complexity of the

world's wind movements we can at least appreciate the skill and research involved in those meteorological observations which produce our weather forecasts.

The name "trades"—short for "trade winds"—does not come from their usefulness to commerce in sailing-ship days, but from the nautical expression "to blow trade", meaning to blow regularly. They are the steady, faithful winds of the world, as opposed to the flirtatious and fickle ones, and they occur in all open seas on both sides of the equator, and to a distance of about thirty degrees north and south of it. In the days of the old wind-jammers they were certainly of the greatest value in navigation.

When a sailing-ship came into a trade wind belt it could depend on making steady progress. The trade wind might be moderate, or no more than a breeze, but if the ship was sailing with the wind full advantage could be taken of it, by rigging extra sails at the ends of the yards, giving a broadened stretch of canvas which caught every capful of moving air.

Although seamen of a century or so ago had every reason to appreciate the trade winds more than we do today, the scientific explanations of the trades in those days were often little short of ludicrous. One commonly accepted hypothesis was that as the atmosphere was carried round by the earth the lower layers managed to keep pace with it, but the higher regions "dragged" or were left behind altogether, so that disturbances near the land and sea surfaces were caused by the "lag". Some authorities, even as recently as a century ago, believed that the "lag" caused a continual breeze from east to west, along the equatorial belt. But such "explanations" of the trades, erroneous as they are now known to be, are practical and scientific indeed compared with one hypothesis seriously put forward by a certain Dr. Lister, in the *Philosophical Transactions* (Vol. 156) at the beginning of the nineteenth century.

Dr. Lister conjectured that the tropical or trade winds arose, in great part, from "the daily and constant exhalations of a sea-plant, called the *sargossa*, or *lenticula marina*" —a weed which will be noticed in a later chapter— "which grows in vast quantities from 36° to 18° north latitude, and elsewhere upon the deepest seas. For the matter of wind, coming from the breath of only one plant, must needs be constant and uniform; whereas the great variety of trees and plants on land furnishes a confused matter of winds. Hence it is that the winds are briskest about noon, the sun quickening the plant most then, and causing it to breathe faster and more vigorously." The worthy doctor—and this was in the year 1818—went on to say that "every plant is, in some measure, an heliotrope,* and bends itself, and moves after the sun, and consequently emits its vapour thitherward; so that the direction of the trade wind is, in some measure, also in the course of the sun."

Among other curious ideas about winds, commonly held in the eighteenth century, was the belief that, in England, the west wind was most frequent about noon, the east in the evening, the south in the night and the north in the morning.

Less than two hundred years ago, some authors on diseases believed that winds could enter and remain within various bones of the human body. A certain Dr. Reyn, for instance, in his *Discourse on the Gout*, wrote that "flatuses, or winds, enclosed between the periosteum and the bone, are the true cause of that disease—this wind being of a dry, cold and malignant nature". He was also of the opinion that "headaches, palpitations of the heart, toothache, pleurisy, convulsions, colics, and many other diseases, are originally due to the same cause—the various motions and determinations of the winds, which denominate diseases from the places which are the scenes of their action".

*A name given originally to any plants with flowers which turn to follow the sun.

The spinning of the earth on its axis is the primary cause of the complexities in the wind systems. If the earth did not rotate, the heated air rising from the world's equatorial belt would be constantly replaced by cool air flowing towards the belt from the poles, which air would be warmed and uplifted again by the sun's heat, and again replaced by more cool air—thus a steady circulation of air would be maintained. But any such "merry-go-round" circulation of the world's winds is interfered with and made extremely complicated by the fact that the earth itself is a "roundabout".

The air above the equator is carried round with its spinning surface at 1,000 miles an hour—making a complete revolution every twenty-four hours—while the air above each of the poles is (theoretically) stationary. Between the equator and the poles the air rotates at varying speeds. The effect of all this can be seen in the trade winds. If the world's vast globe were at rest the winds would blow north and south from the equator, under the influence of the sun's rays. The earth's spin gives the main winds—the trades—a twist to the right in the northern hemisphere and to the left in the southern hemisphere.

So the winds of the world "go like clockwork" and in fact so much like clockwork that they are like a train of geared wheels, all working together. The simile is fairly accurate, for there are other influences on the working of a clock than the gearing of its wheels; so it is with the winds.

There is, for instance, the pendulum-like effect of the alternation of day and night, in its regular modification of the "escapement" of the surface heat of the world's land and sea areas.

The world's winds rage across both land and water surfaces, so that they are affected by the great contrasts of temperature between the continents and the neighbouring oceans, which set up wind systems of their own.

...ad of sawfish, caught off ...getta Islands, near New ...nea. The formidable "saw" ...two uses: as a trowel to ...b out edible creatures from ...sea bed, and as a fearsome ...hed weapon of offence and ...ence. The sawfish is often ...fused with the swordfish ...low) but the creatures' ...pons should clearly indicate ...appropriate names: that of ...sawfish tears and flays, ...le the swordfish's weapon thrusts and pierces.

(Black Sto...

Above: *the curiously named "chicken fish"—a weird sea creature avoided by other f̲
If touched by a harpoon the creature feels so sure of its dreaded armament that it moves a̲
slowly, as if scorning attack, and is easily captured.* Below: *the* bêche-de-mer,
cucumber or trepang—eaten as a luxury by the Chinese.

These are fairly well defined, especially in the southern hemisphere which comprises most of the world's sea-surface and so is free from the disturbances and irregularities of the land areas.

At the equator there is a low-pressure belt, long known to mariners as the doldrums. There are actually other regions of the world where the winds are never very strong, and where long periods of calm can be expected, particularly at the poles and near the tropics, but the calm belt near the equator has gained a reputation for deadly calm and the name "doldrums" has been associated with it for more than a century and a half. Yet a companion word, "tantrums" would be more appropriate to describe the "atmosphere" of the equatorial area we are considering. For the doldrums do as they please and are not only liable to fits of sulks but to outbursts of violent temper. It was in the doldrums that the phantom ship of Coleridge's *Ancient Mariner* lay becalmed: "a painted ship upon a painted ocean", while the pitch sluggishly oozed out of her heated seams and food and water ran perilously short. In the pioneer days of the Australian emigrant traffic, before steamers burst their boilers on American rivers, the doldrums earned the unhappy title of "the wayside grave"; for numbers of passengers, becalmed in ships which had ineffectually struggled to emerge from the merciless grip of the windless calm, gave up the struggle and died in the placid waters.

The doldrums vary in size as well as in character. They are about 100 miles in breadth in February, as an area of deathly stillness, and 300 miles in breadth in August. Yet the area may change, treacherously, to a region of storm, vicious squalls, thunder, lightning and torrential rain. In the old windjammer days a ship might drive through the doldrums in a single day, lashed forward by spiteful winds and buffeted by raging seas; or she might linger there for weary weeks, "ghosting" a mile or so now and then as her cursing crew handled her lofty royals and skysails to little effect.

Fortunately for the mariners of those days, they knew where they were if they kept to the trades, north or south of the doldrums. One of the first of the world's mariners to discover the reliability of the trades was Columbus. It was with their assistance that he was able to discover America, even as Magellan used them later to sail across the Pacific. But the steadiness of the winds, which helped Columbus and his crew to gain their outward objective, caused Columbus serious trouble after his ship had turned round and was sailing in the other direction. For the superstitious crew expected the wind to turn with them and blow them safely home again.

When they found that it stubbornly refused to reverse its direction to please them, they declared that the Almighty was angry with them for having discovered America and its secrets and was even using His winds to show His displeasure. Columbus had all he could do to control a crew so enthusiastic on the outward voyage, when success was still a matter of risk and peril, and so ungrateful and inconsistent on the homeward voyage, with success assured.

In each hemisphere there are three wind zones—one formed by winds which blow slantwise from the polar regions to the equator, another by winds which blow slantwise from the equator to the pole, and a third formed by winds that blow mainly from west to east. In the northern hemisphere these are north and south of the horse latitudes, which lie between 30° and 35° north. The name "horse latitudes" (applied to a sea area which, like that of the doldrums, is often becalmed) has been passed down from the world's sailing-ship days, when there was a considerable trade in horses between England and Jamaica. It often happened that ships loaded with horses were so long delayed in these regions by lack of wind that water ran very short. To conserve it the crews would sacrifice some or even all of the horses—overboard the poor creatures had to go, to swim vainly for a while near the becalmed ships and then drown. Seen as the light fades at eventide, charging towards us across the ocean's surface, the white-crested waves—often called "white horses"—remind us of those tragic happenings in the horse latitudes of years ago.

The British Isles lie in the region of the westerly winds, which moderate the severity of our winters, owing to the fact that the winds have to cross comparatively warm stretches of the Atlantic. When the westerlies fail, which can happen for various reasons, this country can be invaded by cold easterly winds from across Europe. In happier circumstances the horse latitudes (following the sun northwards) can extend their calmer influence to our coasts and bring us dry "Mediterranean" weather.

But the westerly winds can be as pitiless as the easterly ones, though in different ways. When they lash the Atlantic to fury they can do considerable damage along Britain's coasts—as they did in the terrible gales of 1824, when gigantic waves tossed five-ton lumps of stone over Plymouth breakwater as though they were children's building blocks.

The winds of the world can be as gentle as little children or as malevolently violent as bloodthirsty giants.

In the northern hemisphere, the warm, moist north-ward-flowing winds encounter cool ones from the wide expanses of Siberia in a zone which lies just off the coast of Asia over the Pacific Ocean. This causes a vast south-west to north-east disturbance, long known as the "Asiatic jet". As a result storms originate in the zone about every three days which pass on a rhythmic motion to the overlying westerlies. These troughs and crests of pressure, resembling sea-waves, move towards North America, but before they reach it they are reinforced by disturbances to the west of the continent, in a zone which extends northward to Alaska.

On the continent itself is another zone of disturbance, east of the Rockies, where warm, moist winds from the Gulf meet cool Pacific ones, dried by their passage over the mountains. There are other zones of disturbance, so that the Asiatic jet, receiving its main "drive" from the sun, is affected by auxiliary forces arising in the other zones. Complicated though it becomes, the process continues rhythmically in a kind of "wind routine" which can be used as one of the permanent factors in the data studied by experts in forecasting the world's weather.

Water-vapour is generally present in the air in greater or lesser quantities. If pure, dry air—that is, air from which all dust and traces of electricity have been removed —is mixed with pure water-vapour, and the resulting mixture cooled below the temperature of saturation, condensation does not take place. But if fine dust is injected into the pure mixture, without altering its temperature or pressure, a fine mist is at once developed. A charge of electricity introduced into the mixture will also cause condensation. The colder the air, the less water it can hold in the form of invisible vapour. A pound of air at ninety degrees can hold as much as half an ounce of water-vapour, but at freezing point it can only hold a sixteenth of an ounce : the air is fully saturated at that temperature with that amount of moisture.

The air may be chilled as it passes up the surface of a mountain, or as a current rising from a warm surface, or it may be forced up the sloping surface of a mass of cooler, heavier air. If no dust particles were present the rising air might become overloaded (or "supersaturated") with water molecules without cloud forming —but the dust particles are almost always present in vast numbers. When the saturated air becomes too cold to sustain the number of water molecules present, these converge on the dust particles to form droplets—but still averaging only one three-thousandth of an inch in diameter. These, in quadrillions, are spaced so widely apart that they form a misty veil in the sky which is just visible.

More and more droplets are formed, and these gradually merge into actual raindrops which fall to the earth—each drop containing anything up to a million of the original droplets. We know that the whole process of rain- or snowflake-formation is one of repeated associations. In one sense the water-droplets act like humans who form small assemblies which join others to form larger groups, and so on, until huge "mass meetings" are held—the process is one of widening co-operation.

Apart from the trades and similar winds which are the "master mariners", ceaselessly engaged in their routine voyagings over the surfaces of the oceans, there are numbers of winds which confine their activities to local areas.

Even as men and women are classified according to their various occupations, so winds are classified according to their speeds. Sir Francis Beaufort devised a scale in 1805 which is still used for measuring wind velocities. It allocates numbers to winds in accordance with their differing strengths, from "light air" (1), upwards through "slight breeze" (2), "gentle breeze" (3)—a wind of eight to twelve miles an hour—to wind number 12, a hurricane moving at "greater than seventy-five miles an hour". Such terrific winds are only very rarely experienced. Even wind number 10—"whole gale"—blowing at between fifty-five and sixty-three miles an hour—is one seldom experienced inland, trees being uprooted and considerable structural damage being caused; although winds of this velocity were experienced at Weymouth, England, as recently as May 1957.

Although the Beaufort scale ends with wind number 12, and winds over seventy-five miles an hour are certainly rare, hurricanes moving at speeds considerably in excess of that figure have been recorded. The maximum wind velocity recorded in the British Isles was 125 miles an hour at Costa Hill, Orkneys, on 31st January 1953. But calculations from the enormous destruction caused by tornadoes show that they can easily surpass 500 miles an hour.

A tornado which visited Mayfield, Ohio, U.S.A., on the 4th of February 1842 struck with a fury that has probably never been equalled in the history of modern civilization. It was calculated by authorities of the time to have a velocity of 682 miles an hour. Although the figure has been disputed, there is no doubt that the wind reached a velocity on that occasion many times greater than that of ordinary tornadoes—if any tornado can ever be described as "ordinary".

Compared with such a wind, the Mistral—a cold, dry wind which blows from the north-west in the Gulf of Lyons, and which has often been described as a plague— seems but a gentle zephyr. It blows for varying periods— sometimes for as long as ninety days, is confined to the coastal districts, and is announced by white "cottony" clouds which suddenly appear in a serene sky.

The Bora is a wild, bleak wind that rushes down from the Alps to the Adriatic and the Black Sea. It is a deafening, deadly wind, that has been known to overturn heavy wagons and even carry horses and drivers great distances.

Of the hot winds the dreaded Simoom of northern Africa and Arabia is best known. Heralded by an evil-looking yellow hue on the horizon, the Simoom raises great clouds of dust and adds serious hardship to a desert journey. The Sirocco of Sicily and Southern Italy is a similar wind, but is less dry, being tempered by its passage across the Mediterranean. Another hot wind is the Harmattan, prevalent along the coast of Guinea and below Cape Verde and Cape Lopez at certain times in the year.

Monsoons occur in the China Sea and the Indian

Ocean, but the term can be applied to other seasonal winds. Independently of their value in bringing rain to countries which would otherwise degenerate into deserts, they are, like the trades, useful for navigation. In sailing-ship days, mariners would plan their voyages to take advantage of them, and even in the early days of steam-ships their captains would take them into account and often achieve the feat of running before them: to the dis-comfort of their passengers, but with good effect on the times of their voyages.

The world's oceans and winds are in close sympathy. They form an alliance in which it might seem that the oceans are the sleeping partners, and the winds the active ones who do nearly all the work regarding the transport of countless millions of tons of waste matter to the sur-faces of the sea, and the movement of innumerable clouds which discharge themselves into the oceans.

Winds are forever moving over the world in numerous directions, and currents of air are continually ascending and descending, and in all that they do, they are helping the sea to conquer the land, not merely in its erosions of the world's coasts, but also in its reception of millions upon millions of tons of surface soil and dust carried into it by the winds. But the ocean contributes a vital share to the partnership. It gives its surface moisture to the winds, which carry its evaporations far over the world's land surfaces. In exchange for the solid matter that it receives from the land it returns a small percentage of its surface water; the partnership is thus not entirely one-sided. Nevertheless, the sea has the best of the bargain, for the land does not retain the sea's water contributions for long.

The erosive action of winds can be extremely serious. To take but one example: The winds continually blow-ing across the southern half of Australia are removing hundreds of thousands of tons of top-soil every year. Extending northwards from the Mallee district of north-

71

western Victoria is a large area, the surface of which is covered with red dust as fine as flour. This dust is constantly lifted into the air by winds, and deposited again, but enormous quantities of it are blown about the world—in the autumn the south-east trades carry some of it as far as the Dutch East Indies, while westerly winds often carry it far out over the Tasman Sea. Samples taken from the sea-floor in that area show the presence of it in deposits of red sludge. Storms have often carried soil from the world's land surfaces far out into the ocean.

Transporting material is one of the principal tasks of the world's winds. As "dustmen" they seem determined to get as much "waste material" from the earth's land surfaces into the sea as possible. The sea is their ultimate dumping ground. The material they carry (dusts and pollens of all kinds) may go up to the skies and come down again, but at long last the insatiable ocean must receive large quantities of it, taking it down to the sea-beds.

The dust thrown into the air by the eruption of the Krakatoa volcano, in the Sunda Strait between Java and Sumatra, in 1883, when the resulting tidal wave drowned 36,000 people, caused brilliant sunsets in all countries for years afterwards as it drifted around the world, most of it coming to rest at last in the world's oceans.

CHAPTER V

THE MOVING WATERS

ALL disturbances of the world's waters, whether caused by a stone tossed into a pond, by the prow of an ocean liner, or by a mighty seismic upheaval of the sea bed, are subject to uniform laws. Ripples, waves, rollers, tides, bores and tidal waves are classifications of sea and river movements which help us to understand them better, but they are all governed by the same inflexible principles.

The world's winds are the primary causes of surface disturbances of the oceans, rivers and streams, and they constantly build up minor movements into larger ones. But although one would expect that the slightest breath of air would ruffle a water surface with very small waves, this does not happen: there is a limit to what the wind can do. A breeze moving at two knots (12,160 feet an hour) or under cannot raise even the tiniest waves on any water surface. But when it is moving at just over two knots it produces the very smallest waves that can exist on the sea. These minimum wavelets always have the same wave-length—three inches from the crest of one wavelet to the crest of the next—they cannot measure less. Nor can they travel at a slower speed than fourteen inches a second. But from that basic size and basic speed they can be built up by the wind, which does not merely push them but also pulls at them, so that ripples can become formidable waves, which can again be merged into larger movements—breakers, tidal waves and so on.

Seamen have a rough and ready method of forecasting the size of the waves which may be expected under gale conditions. They call the uninterrupted distance over which a wind has been building up the "fetch". Short fetches produce small waves—long fetches can produce enormous ones. Taking the square root of the fetch (measured in nautical miles) seamen multiply it by one and a half, and this gives them, in feet, the height of the waves which the wind is building up across the fetch. This simple formula proves remarkably reliable in forecasting the approaching wave heights on widely varying stretches of water—even up to fetches several hundreds of miles in extent.

Those who go down to the sea in ships have many other methods of estimating the height and force of waves. So with inland waterways. Canal navigators know that there is a certain speed at which a canal boat may be propelled, for it rides on a wave and is carried forward by it, and if a calculation is made which takes all factors into consideration the speed can be maintained with the least additional expenditure of power.

The mathematical formulae covering wave motion—whether in aeroform bodies, in solid bodies, or in liquids—are vastly complex, but there is a simple, straight-forward relationship between sea waves and their speed which is not hard to understand. In this relationship the *height* of a wave, strangely enough, does not come into it. The formula is simply this: That the speed (in feet per second) of any wave is equal to the wave-length (the distance from one wave-crest to the next) divided by the time that elapses (in seconds) between successive waves as they pass any fixed point. Using this formula—which is easier to apply in practice than might appear as you read it—you can calculate the speed of any wave when you are by the sea.

The infinitely complicated movements of the sea's

surface waters are constantly breaking up the world's coastlines and carrying material away from the shores, but the breakers and rollers are only responsible for a part of the land material which the sea receives. It has enormous power, infinite patience, and an insatiable appetite—an appetite which is fed not only by its own efforts, but by its numerous allies. Forever and forever, growing in size and strength as they labour, the world's streams and rivers carry sediment down to the sea, robbing the land—sediment which the sea greedily swallows, its monstrous appetite unappeased.

The Mississippi alone carries down the Gulf, day by day and every day, over a million tons of sediment. Professor Salisbury, in his great work *Physiography*,* says: "It would take nearly 900 daily trains of fifty cars each, and each car carrying twenty-five tons, to carry an equal amount of sand and mud to the Gulf. All the rivers of the earth are perhaps carrying to the sea forty times as much as the Mississippi." This estimate gives us a mental picture of sediment being carried into the oceans *every day* amounting to over forty million tons.

Professor Salisbury makes the significant statement that "Every drop of water which falls on the land has for its mission the getting of the land into the sea". He is not exaggerating when he says that this is the main task of the world's rivers.

Perhaps the Yangtse Kiang and the Hwang Ho are the two rivers which are the most active levellers of the world's continents. The former carries to the sea three times as much sediment as the Ganges. Fabre, in his fascinating work *This Earth of Ours*,† estimates that the matter carried into the sea by the Yangtse Kiang is even greater than that carried into the sea by the Mississippi. He uses shiploads, instead of trainloads, to illustrate his statement: "For conveyance by vessel of this

*Murray, 1907.
†Fisher Unwin, 1923.

immense mass of silt there would be required a fleet of 2,000 ships, each with a capacity of 1,400 tons, and they would have to descend the river daily and throw their cargoes into the sea." Fabre, in all his books, was a careful and reliable investigator, and he evidently gave much painstaking research to this question of the amount of sediment carried into the sea by the Yangtse Kiang. Of the Hwang Ho he said: "It amasses at its mouth every twenty-five days enough sediment to make an island a kilometre square, and it threatens to fill up the vast gulf into which it empties."

Despite these facts, the rushing influx of water from the world's streams and rivers overwhelmingly exceeds in volume the amount of soil and silt that the ocean receives. The sea returns the land's gifts so munificently that it makes the land look like a poor relation. Incredibly old, it has all the time it needs as it crumbles and batters the world's coastlines. Cliffs break away, boulders and rocks crash down, rocks become pebbles and pebbles are broken down into sand. Fossils of creatures which once lived in the sea deeps have been found in rocks 15,000 feet above the surface: but the sea has only loaned them to the land, knowing that they must be repaid with interest.

The sea has allies other than its rivers and streams and currents. It has its ice-caps. Every 100 years the melting of these releases such a vast volume of water into the world's oceans that it raises the sea another eight inches. The melting of the ice-caps is a natural process which is being considerably accelerated by mankind's use of oil and gas as fuel, the burning of which is discharging gases that are warming the atmosphere around the earth to a height of as much as sixteen miles. Some authorities calculate that, if this acceleration continues, the ocean levels will rise at least forty feet and flood huge areas—particularly such low-lying areas as South Florida, parts of New York City, downtown San Francisco, and much of Tokyo, where there is little or no land forty feet above sea-level.

The sediment brought down into the sea by rivers, together with the water continually delivered into it by melting ice-caps (in fact everything received by the sea) is forever churned and widely distributed by the currents of the ocean. Little is known of the forces which originate the deep-water movements. The layering of the under-water surfaces, and the directions in which their water masses travel may be determined by heating, cooling, evaporation and rainfall. There is much uncertainty about the speeds of the deep currents—some authorities give them speeds a hundred times as great as those of other authorities. Human knowledge is built up, like a coral reef, laboriously and slowly.

Countless millions of tiny creatures contribute their individually insignificant efforts to the building of a reef. They labour unseen and their task might, in its earliest stages, seem impossible. Yet their co-operative efforts bring the reef to the surface at last, and far above it. So the labours of innumerable humans (many of them fated to live and die unknown to the world) result in an accumulation of knowledge which at long last emerges into the light.

There are many similarities between ocean and at-mospheric conditions, and of these one of the most sig-nificant is the existence of rotatory movements in both. There are wheels within wheels in the atmosphere and wheels within wheels in the sea.

The currents of the Atlantic may be roughly simplified into two circling streams: one turning clockwise in the North Atlantic and the other spinning anti-clockwise in the South Atlantic. The Gulf Stream is part of the North Atlantic "whirlpool", a system of currents called by the ancients "Oceanus" or the "Ocean River". The word "river", applied to the North Atlantic stream is a com-monplace one concealing a fact which challenges the imagination, for seventy-five million tons of water are transported past any given spot in the vast circular stream in every second of time.

The Gulf Stream is a section of the largest "water wheel" in the world. As the earth turns on its axis at a thousand miles an hour, the Ocean River, moving within the vast envelope of water which clings to the spinning earth, is also turning, but far more sluggishly, for the average rate of its revolution is three or four miles an hour only. Yet it spins, day after day and century after century: a mighty river of water carrying thousands of ships on its surface and countless myriads of living creatures within its swirling depths.

Complicated by the entrance and exit of innumerable currents and counter-currents, eddies, tributaries and other forms of moving water, the great Wheel River of the North Atlantic, under the lash of the trades, runs towards the American continent in a westerly direction, and might girdle the globe itself if its flow were not checked and channelled by the interposed land-masses and sent spinning clockwise by the earth's rotary motion.

There are surfaces below the sea's actual surface. These are formed by layers of water of different densities in the ocean deeps—the upper area of each layer being a surface in contact with the lower area of the layer above it. These concealed surfaces are—like the more generally known surface of the ocean itself—traversed by waves. The waves are caused by rhythmic undulations which pass over the concealed surfaces, and they dwarf the greatest waves ever recorded on the actual surface of the sea above them. Exhaustive temperature measurements have shown that the ocean's concealed surfaces are rising and falling incessantly as waves which often reach heights of as much as 300 feet. The cause of these submarine waves, far down in the deeps, is quite unknown to us, but we do know that their movements affect the complicated inter-relationships of the currents nearer the surface, and the tides and tidal waves of the oceans.

In all the world's seas, currents are wheeling slowly in movements which have carried the waters round and round incessantly for countless centuries. Taken over a long period, the precision of such complicated movements justifies the use of the phrase: "like clockwork". The "mainspring", empowering all the complicated movements, is the sun's heat, but the "escapement", controlling the power, is the tidal and current system of the oceans, for the winds, transmitting the power, can only be likened to a carefully calculated "train" of clockwork wheels, of which the trades are the largest. In this analogy, the Gulf Stream fits in as the escapement wheel itself, which steadily releases the power transmitted by the wheels from the mainspring.

Using six ships, which zigzagged, 150 miles apart, in and out of the surface of the Gulf Stream, an expedition organized by the U.S. Navy Hydrographic Office in 1951 surveyed a part of the course of that enormous body of water as it swept between Cape Hatteras and the Grand Banks.

The Gulf Stream issues from the Gulf of Mexico under tremendous pressure, caused by its confined passage through the Florida Strait, runs parallel with the American coast as far as Newfoundland and then sweeps on in the direction of Europe and Africa, splitting into four separate branches of the main river of water. Until the U.S. Navy's expedition, the course of the Stream had not been accurately checked for any considerable part of its length. The survey elicited some fascinating facts.

The ships used radar to check their positions, and the flow and varying temperature of the moving waters were carefully measured at intervals. The maximum speed of the Gulf Stream over the area was found to be six miles an hour—higher than the average speed of the Stream over its entire course. The great pressure imposed upon the waters before they emerged from the Gulf is evidently the cause of this. Off Cape Hatteras the Stream wriggled around like a snake released from a box, enjoying its newly-found freedom, sometimes getting off its course as much as eleven miles in a day's wandering. In the surveyed area, the Stream was found to have a temperature of seventy-five degrees, and to be about fifteen miles wide and a mile deep, carrying over a thousand times as much water in its course as the mighty Mississippi.

We have followed the south equatorial current over one part of its journey only. Before the vast body of water is forced onward into the Atlantic it twists and turns and doubles back in a curiously sinuous course. In the Gulf of Mexico the pressure of its volume is so great that its level is eight inches higher there than it is on the Atlantic coast of Florida. Through the ninety-mile gap between Florida and Cuba this irresistible ocean river pours more than 100,000 million tons of water every minute.

Its beneficent influence on the climate of Western Europe, without which Britain would suffer ice-bound winters, must not blind us to the potential malevolence of this mighty equatorial current if its waters were reinforced by the melting of the ice-caps in any considerable measure.

Before we consider the extraordinary whirlpool of weeds, populated by all kinds of interesting creatures, which lies in the centre of the Gulf Stream's circular course and is known as the Sargasso Sea, we must examine some of the ocean's tides and tidal waves.

Tides are caused by the co-operation of the gravitational influences of the sun and moon on the world's waters. The partnership is a strange one. Our earth and the moon, separated by (roughly) a quarter of a million miles, are of course mutually attracted, and in their mutual attraction they waltz like a couple on a dance floor, circling each other and also moving in a vast circle around the sun, which is pulling at them both.

It is a well-known fact that the gravitational force of

the sun and moon attracts the earth's waters which lie closest to them. This pull, however, is so small compared with that of the earth's pull on those same waters that they are not pulled vertically away from the earth's surface. The further we move away from this nearest point, however, the more horizontal does the joint pull of the sun and moon become. Obviously it takes far less force to make the water move horizontally over the earth's surface than to draw it up vertically, and so the water is drawn from all directions to this nearest point until it is piled up. This bulge is high tide. It is not so easy to see why the water on the *opposite* side should bulge outward, *away* from the sun or moon. Realize that the earth itself is pulled away from those far-side waters and the matter becomes clearer. It should now be obvious that the highest tides will occur when the sun and moon are on the same side of the earth, pulling together, and when they are directly opposite each other with the earth between.

Such conditions occur only at intervals, between which the sun and moon are pulling at constantly varying angles. The movements of the tides are also complicated by the fact that (as seen from our point of view on this earth) the sun and moon do not go round the earth in unison but at different speeds. The lunar day is one of 24.84 hours, compared with the solar day's 24. This apparent "lag" of the moon compared with the sun causes the difference in the daily times of high tides.

When you spend your holiday at the seaside and get up before breakfast for a swim you find the sea further and further out as mornings pass. As a rule the high tides around Great Britain are about fifty minutes later each day.

That there are two tides each day, and not one is due to the rotation of the earth so that each place experiences high water when it is nearest and furthest from the moon; and so, through all its phases, the tides are duplicated, one on each side of the earth, with the result that any part of the world's coastline affected by tides has two tides a day. As the moon's phases take a lunar month to go through, the large spring tides occur fortnightly.

Sweeping round the world, the tides caused by the sun and moon in this strange triangular association with the earth, are influenced by land configurations and many other factors. In confined channels the rushing currents of water may be terrifyingly powerful. Where any strong current races over rough, shallow ground, or where two currents meet, the fierce and noisy condition known as "tide-rip" may be created, or actual whirlpools may occur, menacing shipping and human life.

So many factors control the movements of tidal waters that calculations designed to predict their future behaviour need to be so complex that they might seem, at first thought, to be mathematically impossible. Such calculations can only be compared with those made by astronomers in forecasting the movements of stars, planets and comets, yet oceanographers in the world's meteorological observatories and institutes—particularly at Liverpool and Birkenhead—have used tidal information collected in past centuries with such good effect that their calculations enable them to predict with accuracy how tides will run in various parts of the world for many years ahead. Unexpected happenings may disturb some of their calculations and produce tidal waves causing considerable damage, but the fact remains that ships of all nations are able to time their movements by reference to tide-tables which are a monumental tribute to the patience and intellectual skill of meteorological experts.

The waves which break rhythmically on seaside beaches in calm weather are subject to laws which have been studied and analysed by man, even as the huge tidal waves which swoop down upon coastal places at rare intervals and cause great damage and loss of life are also subject to known laws, although the movements of the former may be to some extent predictable, while those of the latter are erratic and cannot be forecast.

The fearful velocities of surface storms might be instanced with numbers of cases. One of the most remarkable in recent years was the cyclone which hit Belsize, the capital of British Honduras, in 1931. Striking the town at 2.30 p.m. on 10th September, the hurricane destroyed the town in half an hour—all the churches were wrecked and not a building was left undamaged. The wind sometimes reached a velocity of 150 miles an hour. A 200-ton dredger was lifted from the sea and dropped squarely on the roof of the Customs House. That single incident exemplifies the force of storms over the sea, although, mercifully, few storms are as violent.

Tidal waves may be caused by mighty winds, or by earthquakes or settlements of the sea-bed, deep down under the waves. On 10th November 1932, a tidal wave twenty feet in height swept inland over Cuba and other West Indian islands. The cyclone which accompanied it raged with a velocity of 200 miles an hour, destroying houses, stores, crops—almost everything in its path. Some 3,000 people were drowned or otherwise killed at Santa Cruz del Sur, and the town was completely destroyed. The tidal wave carried numbers of bodies and a considerable amount of wreckage back into the sea.

The Humber and the Mersey are examples of Britain's tidal rivers. In some instances, where the tide comes in swiftly and the river runs rapidly, the water moving inland from the sea may be heaped up to several feet in height, instead of moving up the river steadily and with a gradual increase in the height of the water. Such a wave —which can be a most exciting thing to watch—is paradoxically called a "bore", meaning a billow. In France the name *eau guerre* is given to it (appropriately, for the term means "water war") while in South America it is called *proroca*, "the destroyer".

One of the most notable bores in Great Britain is the one which periodically occurs on the Severn, near the head of the Bristol Channel. The tide, which rises to a height of forty feet, making a most impressive spectacle, rushes up the funnel-shaped Channel in a continuous wave ninety yards in length, and with a crest averaging four or five feet. But the height of the bore's crest varies. In 1932 the moving wall of water was nearly eight feet high. As the bore rushes up the Severn it makes a curious noise, as though it were a living thing speeding forward to capture its prey.

Bores on British rivers include a remarkable one which rushes up the Trent, forming a wave from three to five feet high, and others on the Solent and Dee. In France a wave seven feet high races up the Seine at spring tide, to a distance of forty miles up the river. Another of similar height travels up the river Hooghly in India, while an even higher one—twelve to fifteen feet high—appropriately called the *amassona*, meaning "boat destroyer", sweeps up the Amazon with a roar that can be heard over five miles away.

The world's most remarkable bore occurs on the Tsien-tang-kiang in China. A tidal wave from the Pacific rushes into the estuary, and as the water piles up a bore is created which may be as much as thirty-four feet in height. Its approach can be heard for more than an hour before its arrival, and as it passes the sound has been likened to the roar of Niagara Falls. It rushes by Haining at a speed of over fourteen miles an hour, and it has been calculated that nearly two million tons of water pass that place every minute when the bore is in full spate. The mighty wall of water dies away at last about forty-two miles from the river's mouth.

Although the Tsien-tang-kiang bore is rightly regarded as the world's greatest, there is an area even more remarkable for the great rise and fall of its tides, and for the number of its bores. This is the Bay of Fundy, an inlet of the North Atlantic, separating New Brunswick from Nova Scotia. Its length up to Chignecto Bay is 140 miles and its extreme breadth forty-five miles. The peculiar formation of the bay gives it the greatest tidal range in the world. Its dimensions and shape are exactly right, as a basin which shelves and narrows gradually for the first 100 miles and then divides into two long inlets, to give its waters extreme depth ranges.

All it needs for these is a series of rhythmic impulses— even as the water in a bath, resting upon a curved and sloping base, can be made to swill in rhythmic waves high up on the shallow end by sweeping it regularly with the hand. The ocean tides of the Atlantic coast give the water in the bay the required rhythmic impulses. Rising and falling at the entrance to the bay in twelve-hour periods, the Atlantic tides keep the waters within the bay swinging up and down, so that it really has its own *internal* tides, which are kept in motion by the regular pulsations from outside.

At one time the remarkable tides in this area were attributed solely to the passage of the water into the narrow cul-de-sac, but it is now known that they are due to the Atlantic's rhythmic impulses, and the peculiar situation of the bay upon one of the ocean's cotidal lines, where the tidal periods are practically stationary and periodically regular. It is paradoxical that the Atlantic's regular impulses should create such wide variations in tidal range within the bay. At Passamaquoddy Bay, at the southern end of the Bay of Fundy, the rise and fall is about twenty-five feet. But at the northern end, in the narrow upper reaches, the world's greatest tidal heights are reached, averaging sixty feet and sometimes rising as high as seventy-two feet. Yet just across a narrow isthmus, in the Bay Verte (outside the Bay of Fundy) less than twenty miles from where these world's-highest tides occur, the tide rises only four or five feet.

The estuaries of some of the rivers in the northern

reaches of the Bay of Fundy are often completely drained by the falling tide, so that vast areas of red mud are disclosed. Areas of fertile marshes are situated at the head of the bay. The remains of a submerged forest show that the land has subsided there, in the latest geological period, nearly fifty feet.

The Petitcodiac, which empties into Chepody Bay, at the extreme north-west of the Bay of Fundy, is navigable up to twenty-five miles for ships, and for twelve miles farther at high tide. It is but one of many rivers which empty into the Bay of Fundy which has a tidal bore—a crest varying from three to six feet in height which rushes up the river at certain times. Because of its high tides and the many bores in its rivers, the bay is noted for its navigational perils, especially in its upper reaches.

The gravitational pull of the earth upon its own waters is millions of times greater than the pull of the sun and the moon combined, yet the sun can draw the earth's waters a little way towards it with a force which operates across ninety-three million miles of intervening space, while the moon (infinitely smaller than the sun, yet more powerful in its pull because it is so much nearer to the earth) exercises its invisible power across a distance of nearly a quarter of a million miles.

In the open oceans the water piled up into a tidal wave by the moon's attraction (affected to varying degrees by the pull of the sun) follows the moon as it apparently circles the earth. This true tidal wave (which must not be confused with tidal waves caused by earthquakes or other ocean-floor disturbances) must be measured not in feet or miles but in hours. It is a tidal wave roughly twelve hours and twenty minutes in length (half the time that it takes for the moon to circle the earth—the "circling" being from our viewpoint, of course). The height of the heaped-up water is called "the tidal range". Over the wide oceans this averages about three feet high, and the tidal wave travels at the formidable speed of 500 miles an hour.

Science can only guess how the lives of countless millions of creatures in the world's oceans are affected by the monotonous pulsing of the tides.

Their life durations, their periods of gestation, their habits: all these and many other factors in their multitudinous existences are influenced by the tides on the ocean's surface, and those deeper and more mysterious movements of the undersea waters. Down to the uttermost depths of the world's oceans, through miles of dark water, such tidal influences continue, even as the lives of creatures on the world's land surfaces are influenced by the movements of the distant stars.*

Even as no man lives to himself, so the ocean does not exist as an isolated entity. It is related to the land, the sea and the sky in numerous ways, many of them complicated relationships and some of them very mysterious.

The rains which fall upon its surface do not merely affect the sea's volume as they assist the rivers to replace its continual loss by evaporation: they affect the lives and habits of countless creatures near its surface, and, more remotely, the lives of vast numbers of animals in its depths. So with land erosions, and with the millions of tons of top-soil which are carried into the sea. And so with the winds—they intimately affect life in the oceans.

The tidal waves which follow the moon are not uniformly three feet high—that is the range as the piled-up waters sweep across the oceans under normal conditions. We already have some idea of the tidal range in the Bay of Fundy. As we have seen, it varies throughout the Bay. Other parts of the world—parts of Mexico and Australia, northern France and south-west England—have tidal ranges of as much as twenty feet. Such variations in tidal

*Flammarion and other authors have suggested that ants are guided in their wanderings by the stars; not merely by the light from them, nocturnally, but by mysterious rays, beyond the range of our present knowledge. Birds, bees and other creatures may be guided in their migrations by invisible rays from outer space.

ranges may not seem to have any practical significance. Does it matter to us in our daily lives whether tides in various parts of the world rise only a few feet or to great heights?

The answer is that even today, before man has harnessed the power of the tides to any extent, the world's commerce is considerably affected by tidal ranges.

Vessels of all nations are dependent on the power of the moon to enable them to enter their harbours, for it raises the water for them to cross the harbour bars or dangerous shallows. And so it is wherever industry and shipping have partially harnessed the power of the sea: the rising and falling tides are important factors.

Only a very small part of the sea's enormous power is at present being utilized by man. It is available to him in countless ways, and he is beginning to realize its potentialities, even as he is beginning to harness the world's rivers. Tidal power is already being tapped in many countries. But the power in the world's ocean currents still runs to waste. A single fact can help us to appreciate the volume of that power. The world's strongest ocean currents are those in the Saltfjord, Norway, where they race at nearly nineteen and a half miles an hour. It does not require much imagination to picture the benefits which could be enjoyed by mankind if only a fraction of the power of the ocean's currents could be harnessed.

Man is turning to the peaceful use of atomic energy, realizing that it can eventually produce power so cheaply that the lives of millions can be transformed by it. Coincidentally with the application of atomic power to industrial and domestic uses, men in many nations are devising schemes for using the sun's energy, and— increasingly—the power stored in the world's rivers and waterfalls, and in the sea itself.

We of this generation are therefore watching the inception of a strange partnership—an alliance between the atom, the sun, and the waters of the world, in the service of man. As years pass the alliance will be strengthened by the invention of new devices which will interlink their respective fields of power.

In this alliance the atom is the senior partner; for its inconceivably vast power—creatively and destructively—is the basis of the sun's energy and the fundamental driving force behind all the movements of the waters.

Future generations will probably reap the full benefits of the atom-sun-sea association, as it brings more and more power into man's service—provided always that the senior partner can be subjected to international control.*

The atomic energy stored in the world's oceans is, of course, vast beyond all human comprehension. There are untold billions of billions of ultra-microscopic whirlpools of energy in a pailful of sea-water: each atom being a miniature solar-system with "planets" revolving around a central "sun"; although the analogy fails when we consider the terrific speeds of the electron "planets" as compared with the relatively slow motions of our sun's planets in their orbits.

Enveloping a spinning earth, the world's oceans have whirlpools in myriads within whirlpools: ranging from atomic ones, through vast numbers of those vortices which are so readily created by the world's winds and all other surface disturbances, right up to the mighty whirlpools which spin steadily and permanently in particular areas of the sea's surface. With the lore and magic of these larger whirlpools, and some of the fascinating creatures which inhabit them, we are now immediately concerned.

---

*"The Harwell men are so certain of their findings that work on H-power is already being farmed out to industry. They are certain they have achieved the fantastic temperature of 12,000,000 degrees centigrade with a small-scale controlled H-bomb reaction in an apparatus called Zeta Two. . . . These experiments are likely to lead to the generation of electric power from a form of hydrogen which can be extracted in unlimited quantities from sea water."—*Daily Express*, 16th December 1957.

CHAPTER VI

WHIRLPOOLS

OLD encyclopaedias and works on natural history have very curious ideas about whirlpools. Until about a century ago the idea prevailed that they could be appeased. Ray's *Cyclopaedia*, published in 1819, for instance, describes a marine whirlpool in these terms:

Wherever it appears it is very furious, and boats, &c., would inevitably be drawn into it; but the people who navigate them are prepared for it, and always carry an empty vessel, a log of wood, or large bundle of straw, or some such thing, in the boat with them. As soon as they perceive the whirlpool they toss this within the vortex, keeping themselves out. This substance, whatever it be, is immediately received in the centre, and carried under water; and as soon as this is done the surface of the place becomes smooth, and they row over it with safety; and in about an hour they see the vortex begin again in some other place, usually at about a mile from the first.

Presumably the same vortex, which has apparently been appeased in one place, has gone down into the sea and emerged in another place! The *Cyclopaedia* does not mention more than one "bundle of straw, or some such thing", but it is evident that a number would have to be carried if several whirlpools were to be appeased in one boat trip.

One of the best known whirlpools is the Charybdis.

The word is now almost exclusively associated with the mythological story of Poseidon and Gaea, in which Charybdis stole the oxen of Hercules and was thunder-struck for her offence by Jupiter, who changed her into the whirlpool situated opposite the rock Scylla, at the entrance to the Strait of Messina, thus originating the phrase "between Scylla and Charybdis": meaning between two opposing dangers. Some affirm that Hercules killed her himself; others, that Scylla committed the robbery and was killed for it by Hercules, but that her father Phorcus put Charybdis into a cauldron and stewed her in it for so long that she came to life again. Another (the Homeric account) makes Charybdis a male figure who dwelt under an immense fig-tree on the rock, and swallowed up the waters of the sea three times a day and threw them up again. In all these fables we find the characteristics of actual marine whirlpools. Today, the name of the whirlpool has been changed to Calofaro ("La Rema" is also used). The town on the rock, now known as Scilla, was destroyed by an earthquake in 1908.

But the word "Charybdis" was also used a century or so ago to describe any of certain openings supposed to exist at the bottom of the sea—openings through which its waters are received and conveyed by subterranean circulation under land surfaces, to emerge as fountains and springs.

It was held that if such undersea holes did not exist then the Mediterranean could not be emptied of the enormous quantities of water it receives, so that it would overflow the land of Egypt and other adjacent coasts. It was believed that the greatest of these holes in the sea bed was an immense Charybdis near the Strait's mouth, hidden deeply below the surface, which collected the surplus waters and carried them inland to the spring and fountain sources.

Dismissing such old legends and fables, modern

oceanographic research has revealed facts regarding Charybdis, which outrival any of the old mythologies in fascinating interest.

As we know it today, this locality which we associate with the old mythologies is an area in the Strait of Messina, between Sicily and the Italian mainland, where a rich store of marine life is periodically swept by fierce rotatory currents and strong winds: an area inhabited by myriads of weird creatures.

The whirlpool itself—or rather the series of whirlpools which make up the stretch of turbulent water—turns far more swiftly than the slowly-wheeling Sargasso, but in normal circumstances it is not dangerous to modern shipping, save to small boats and during the times of its maximum tides. From time immemorial the tidal forces of sun and moon have tugged at the waters in the channel (which is not more than 300 feet deep) and moved them northward and southward alternately: even, at certain times and seasons, sideways. This to-and-fro motion of the waters is characteristic of the Charybdis, and while it proceeds rhythmically the lives of its underwater creatures continue normally. But twice a month the "daily round" of their existences is agitated into periods of whirling violence, as the maximum tides turn the flowing waters into raging torrents.

When this happens hosts of organisms are forcibly dragged up from the deeps, and for a few hours numbers of living, half-alive and dead creatures are either consumed by alert sea birds or cast up on the beaches. The forms of life which survive such tidal hammer-blows are in numerous cases either toughened criminals of the deep or animals which have adapted themselves to the thunderous wave-pressures in curious ways, but there are also numbers of creatures which have survived by taking the line of least resistance as "opportunists" of the ocean.

The sabre-toothed viper-fish is one of the most extraordinary fishes in the Charybdis waters. It has a face far more frightening than any tiger's, with staring eyes and a great gaping mouth which has long fangs resembling stalactites and stalagmites rather than teeth. These are incredibly sharp, yet they bend under pressure. Within the fish's cavern-like mouth are light organs which create luminous patches inside the fearsome jaws. Darting here and there among the smaller creatures of the Charybdis, this sabre-toothed viper-fish, although only fourteen inches in length, is a monster by comparison with other creatures.

Some of the shrimps and prawns tossed about in the Strait are among the opportunists—never do they attempt to go against the prevailing stream. They flaunt a variety of colours—vivid shades of all kinds, including purple and flaming red. Many of them can change their colours very rapidly, in fact they are adepts at adaptation. The chromatophores which enable them to make their instantaneous colour-changes are wonderful devices. They fulfil their purpose by expanding and contracting—the contractions concentrate pigment at the middle of the cell: the expansions disperse it again.

The colour-changing devices of such land creatures as the chameleon act much more slowly. These, like those of the shrimps and prawns of the Charybdis, are also accomplished at the will of the animals, but the processes are quite different. The outer portion of the chameleon's skin or epidermis is transparent, and is underlaid by a system of cells filled with granules and oil-drops which appear white or yellow. Beneath these again are large irregular chromatophores filled with black and red pigment granules. The entire mechanism is under the control of the chameleon's nervous system and is much more complicated than this explanation might suggest.

Wonderfully efficient though it is, the chameleon cannot change colour quickly—it requires a little time to adapt itself to any background upon which it is placed. What then must be the ingenuity, the wonderful crafts-manship, displayed in the construction of the colour-changing mechanisms of the shrimps and prawns of the Charybdis? For they can change colour—using a far greater variety of shades than the chameleon—and much more quickly: the shell of any of the creatures may be one colour at one moment, then, in an instant, it has assumed a different one.

Many of the crustaceans in the Strait have flower-like patches on them suggesting varieties of flowers which grow on land, such as asters, carnations, etc. Nowhere in the world is violence and turbulence so intimately associated with beauty as in the Charybdis whirlpools.

Another queer creature found here is the silver hatchet-fish. It has bulging eyes, set closely together in a head that is actually transparent, and the lenses of its eyes are telescopic. Silvery pigment makes the animal's sides blaze with a tinsel-like effect. Seen from below, the hatchet-fish shows only as a narrow blade studded with brilliant lights. Strangely enough, these luminous patches point downward, and cannot be seen from above the fish.

To get an accurate impression of the hatchet-fish's "lamps" as they are carried under its belly, one must think of a section of Indian corn, for they are packed together in two rows much resembling such a section.

Myriads of tiny crab-like creatures, any one of which could hide beneath a grain of rice, busy themselves in the waters of the Charybdis. During night fishing in the Messina district the boats carry lights, and the tiny crustaceans fly across the water in all directions, attracted by the lights, and forming interlacing lightning streaks on the sea's surface. They are attracted by anything luminous: a fact which indicates the purpose of the "lamps" carried by the hatchet-fishes, which consume the tiny crustaceans in enormous quantities.

There is one fascinating creature of the genus *Cyclothone*

which inhabits the Charybdis and is about an inch long, transparent, and which seems (until it opens its mouth) quite innocent and delicate. But when the mouth opens it is enormous in relation to the animal's size: in fact it has a ratio of mouth to body far exceeding that of any other fish. Within its gaping jaws a complete battery of tiny lamps or light-organs is disclosed. The creature can reveal or conceal these lights at will, by simply opening or closing its gigantic mouth. It swims towards its victim in the gloom of the underseas and, facing it, suddenly opens its mouth. Its victim is immediately attracted by the bright lights, and in a split second is drawn past them into the other fish's stomach.

There are small sharks in the Charybdis. One of these, seven inches long when immature, can grow to a maximum length of several feet, although even when fully grown it is still a pygmy compared with sharks of other areas. It is a sea-bed feeder and lives in comparatively shallow waters. Its scales are covered with tiny points which can easily rasp the skin if the fish is handled carelessly when caught.

Another weird creature of the Charybdis is the so-called elephant-headed mollusc. This is a thumb-sized animal which swims upside-down. Like many other animals of the Strait it is transparent. Its head looks very similar to that of an elephant, for it has a long "trunk" through which it takes its food. Its eyes, again, are strangely like elephant's eyes, and from each of them a small silvery appendage hangs which has the appearance of a tear-drop.

The whirlpools of the ocean usually remain in relatively fixed positions, but the Charybdis has moved since ancient times, when it was the subject of so many legends. It no longer swirls near the rock of Scylla, but rotates just over a thousand yards off Cape Peloro Lighthouse, towards the other side of the Strait. And it is now not a single whirlpool but the largest of a series into which the original Charybdis broke up, as the result of violent earthquakes which shook the sea-bed under the Strait.

There are many other whirlpools, some of them of considerable size, scattered over the sea's surface.

Of these the most notable is the Maelstrom, first mentioned in Mercator's Atlas of 1595 and situated off the coast of Norway.

An unquestionable authority—the *Sailing Directions for the Coast of Norway*—says that the Maelstrom is "still the most dangerous tideway in Lofoten, its violence being due, in great measure, to the irregularity of the ground". These are described by the document as "like so many pits in the sea". It repeats the old tradition already mentioned regarding the Charybdis, that if fishermen have time to "throw an oar or other bulky body" into one of the vortices "they will get over it safely: the reason being that when the continuity is broken, and the whirling motion of the sea interrupted by something thrown into it, the water must rush suddenly in on all sides and fill up the cavity.

"For the same reason," the author of *Sailing Directions* continues, "in strong breezes, when the waves break, though there may be a whirling round there can be no cavity. In the Maelstrom boats and men have been drawn down by these vortices, and much loss of life has resulted."

The depth of the water in the vicinity of the Maelstrom —supposed at one time to be too deep for sounding—has been found to be no more than twenty fathoms, with a bottom of rocks and white sand. The current runs with the tides alternately (six hours from south to north, then six hours from north to south) producing the whirlpools of the area: unified and idealized by Poe and other writers on the sea.

We have examined only two of the ocean's whirlpools in any detail. In all of them myriads of strange creatures have their homes, all of them with interesting life-cycles and many of them using devices as wonderful in their

(Black Star)

A squid is apparently unaware of its snake-like enemy's intention to devour it, but the eel may get the worst of the encounter, for battles between these two creatures can result in a fair percentage of victories for the many-armed cephalopods.

(Franz Thorbecke)

An unusual photograph of a remora attaching itself to another fish. The powerful sucker can just be seen under the remora's pointed head, and between it and its host's eye. As a "hitch-hiker" of the underwater highways, the remora is much more

various ways as the ones we have already considered. Stories far more fantastic than any created by Poe in his *Tales of Mystery and Imagination* are being enacted, moment by moment, in all parts of the ocean. Ceaselessly, day and night through the centuries, the tragedies and comedies of the deep have been played, usually in utter darkness, by billions of creatures, struggling against each other, feeding upon each other, yet also co-operating with each other in significant demonstrations of the power of interdependence as a means of survival.

But such tragedies and comedies are not confined to the ocean's surfaces and depths: they are matched by the life-cycles of many other animals which throng the sea's fringes and coastlines.

One movement of the world's waters is gargantuan compared with all other movements of the sea: the enormous, slowly-spinning "whirlpool" in the North Atlantic which men have named (from the peculiar Gulf weed, *Sargassum bacciferum*) the Sargasso Sea.

It is probable that more myths and legends have radiated from it into the literature and folklore of the world than from any other area of land or sea. Its weed-entangled stretches have spawned innumerable accounts of wrecks, of web-footed tribes living in its mysterious, impenetrable hinterland, and of weird and monstrous creatures lurking in its floating islands. Even its area is a mystery. Some writers give it a diameter of a thousand miles, and an area of a million square miles, while others declare that it is as large as Europe, which, by the most conservative calculation, has an area of $3\frac{3}{4}$ million square miles. The truth is that the Sargasso Sea is probably larger than Greenland (839,782 square miles) yet considerably less than the size of Europe.

This makes the Sargasso Sea the largest island in the world—if it can be called an island, or even a floating one.

It was discovered by Columbus on his first voyage,

D

when his ship was held in it for about a fortnight. There are numerous stories of ships being imprisoned in the Sargasso Sea—embedded in the floating weed and unable to escape—but such stories have been largely discounted since the expedition of the *Michael Sars* in 1910, under the direction of Sir John Murray and the Norwegian government, which found the surface covered with patches of weed, with clear spaces through which ships might navigate. It is now evident that the Sargasso is neither a sea nor an island, but a spinning archipelago: a group of many islands of seaweed revolving in a vast whirlpool. These islands may mass together or separate, so that their relative sizes vary continually. It may be that some of the stories of ships being imprisoned in the Sargasso are true, despite the findings of the *Michael Sars* expedition, if (as seems quite probable) numbers of the islands have packed together at various times in the past, imprisoning vessels within the larger masses.

Despite the fact that many of the old legends and descriptions of the Sargasso Sea can be safely dismissed, any conception of it as an enormous mass of floating weed (however distributed) and no more, would be utterly inadequate. Very little is known about it, even today; and strange, inexplicable facts (legions of them) are probably concealed beneath the surface of our accumulated knowledge, even as multitudes of living creatures definitely exist beneath the apparently lifeless surface of the weed itself.

At one time it was thought that the peculiar Gulf weed from which the Sargasso gets its name originally grew on the Bahama and Florida shores, and that it was torn off from the shores long ago by the powerful current of the Gulf Stream. But this explanation of the source of the weed has proved to be one of those apparently satisfactory explanations of some of Nature's mysteries which, in the light of later knowledge, are shown to be mere guesses.

It now seems very doubtful that the Bahama and Florida shores were the original habitat of the weed, which now propagates freely *while floating on the ocean surface*, although it is the natural habit of the larger algae to grow from a base of attachment. Such a base—although it normally provides such algae with no more than an anchorage for its roots—seems absolutely necessary to the existence of such weeds in normal circumstances, so that it is difficult to understand how *Sargassum bacciferum* could have adapted itself to a freely-floating existence, and this existence far from its natural habitat. Torn from its natural home the weed would not survive, much less travel a great distance and establish itself again under conditions so dissimilar from those it had known.

It is not found in the main current outside the Sargasso. It grows only over the Yucatan and Musquito Banks, and is swept from them to the Sargasso Sea by the Gulf Stream—from the beginning to the end of its journey a floating plant. Naturalists have estimated that no less than twenty million tons of weed float upon the surface of the Sargasso Sea, while at least another fifty-six million tons lie below the surface.

Oviedo y Valdés, the Spanish chronicler, appointed historiographer to the New World by Charles V, described the Sargasso as "the seaweed meadows", and the name is as appropriate as any. Humboldt was among those who believed that actual land existed in the Sargasso region, or at least a "fucus-bank", but although chroniclers and naturalists of earlier times had often written of the Sargasso as an area peopled with mermaids and strange monsters, including sea-serpents, science has grown more sceptical in recent years.

H. H. Johnston, in the first part of his work *Wonders of Land and Sea* (1913), says that "the *Michael Sars* expedition disposed of the credibility of these legends"— of strange creatures in the Sargasso—he adds, "or at any rate it is thought to have done so." Perhaps Sir Arthur Shipley, in his book *The Voyage of a Vice-chancellor*, sums up the situation adequately when he says: "An amazing amount of fiction and nonsense has been written about the sargasso-weed, but the truth is actually more unbelievable."

For the more we learn of this vast rotating wilderness (or garden) of weed the more mysterious does it become.

Although we have termed it a whirlpool it revolves very slowly, and as imperceptibly to those who come upon it as the starry heavens in their apparent motion around the pole star. Astronomical comparisons come to the mind as we try to get a mental picture of it. As the vast size of the Nebula in Andromeda makes that sky spectacle seem motionless when viewed through our telescopes, so the size of the Sargasso Sea makes its motion inappreciable, even to those who approach it—the rate at which the vast whirlpool of weed and debris turns is so extremely slow. Yet the currents keep it gradually turning—a surface mass of weed, laced by innumerable channels and populated by multitudes of creatures: a wheeling archipelago at least eight times the size of France.

The weed is extremely buoyant, being the most highly organized of the marine algae, *Fucaceae*—"the rock weeds". They are seaweeds which are usually attached to stones by a discoid hold-fast. But when floating, as the *Sargassum bacciferum*, the weeds have long filiform stems, much branched and with narrow, leaf-like fronds with distinct midribs, and small air-bladders. These are like solitary grapes, and have given rise to the common names, "tropical grapes" and "grape-weed". The stems were much used in South America at one time under the name "goitre-sticks" for the cure of goitre.

Although the weed is so buoyant it loses its buoyancy after a period of from three to five years, when it sinks and disintegrates. But even before that period expires an unusually large wave may sweep the weed down thirty or more feet under the surface, in which case the increased pressure will weaken the walls of the bladders so that they are deflated and cannot rise again. The weed is affected by changing temperatures and is thickest in August.

The bladders are truly amazing devices—tiny "life-belts" which, in their untold millions, literally sustain the life which teems in the vast Sargasso archipelago, *holding up* the colossal tonnage of its floating islands.

The phrase "wheels within wheels", which applies to the world's oceans in all kinds of ways, is peculiarly significant regarding the Sargasso. For it is a slowly spinning wheel containing within it innumerable smaller ones—miniature whirlpools at the junctions of the numerous channels of clear water which lace and interlace the floating weed. The channels are really streams of water, running in many directions, and wherever they meet, small whirlpools are formed which are worthy of the name, for they are often swift enough to be dangerous to small craft.

There can be no doubt that the Sargasso Sea is changing its position. Maps of eighty or one hundred years ago show that the weed was met within seven degrees north of the equator, and in fifteen degrees W. longitude. But *Sargassum* is not seen today within six hundred miles of these positions. The weeds, which migrated as individuals across hundreds of miles of ocean and formed an enormous colony, have been moving as a colony ever since. Although large stretches of the whirlpool are still unexplored, and very little is known about such areas, there are now trade routes right through the heart of the Sargasso Sea, mostly traversed by battleships and tramp steamers, for passenger services very rarely pass through it.

Some writers have described the Sargasso as resembling a vast garden, full of ever-multiplying weeds. The analogy is a loose one and only superficially correct, for the "soil" of the Sargasso is the tangled weed itself, and no garden on land is peopled with such great numbers of living creatures. Amid the masses of seaweed there are untold myriads of them—fantastic creatures in swarming millions—busily engaged in their own peculiar activities among the tangled stems and the tropical "grapes", and breeding in the rotting wreckage that has been steadily drawn into the maw of the mighty whirlpool.

Yet contrary to general belief the Sargasso is not inhabited by vast varieties of fish: the species are remarkably limited, as if numerous types avoid the area. The fishes that are found among the weeds are limited to a comparatively small number of species, and are usually smaller in size than species of similar kinds swarming in other parts of the ocean. It has been suggested that the small fishes which are the natural food of sharks have found sanctuary in the Sargasso. Captain C. C. Dixon, an authority on such matters when he made the statement, declared that sharks are never found within the area of the weeds, and that certain types of fishes, realizing this, have escaped into the Sargasso, where they are safe from their chief enemy.

Some authorities estimate that ninety per cent of the wreckage of the oceans eventually finds its way into the Sargasso Sea, making it the world's greatest rubbish tip. Under every piece of partly-submerged wreckage is to be found a creature appropriately called the wreck-fish. This is another name for the stone bass (*Polyprion americanus*) which makes all kinds of flotsam its headquarters, emerging for feeding purposes. It is a brownish fish, of ghoulish appearance as it lurks like a footpad near the sea alleys of the whirlpool, and only two species are known.

Certain varieties of file-fish and flying-fish are also found—the latter often seen skimming over the surface of the weed, and (according to mariners) much more

easily caught than other flying-fishes. One particular
species of flying-fish, peculiar to the Sargasso, is a small
creature only two or three inches long, yellowish-brown
and therefore practically invisible against the weeds. It
lays its eggs in strings resembling pearl necklaces, which
are securely attached to the *Sargassum* leaves and
branches.

The hatchlings soon make themselves at home in their
jungle home, and drift round with the enormous roundabout as it slowly revolves.

Mixed among the weeds of the Sargasso Sea are
hydroids (relatives of jelly-fish and sea-anemones, which
grow into branching colonies by budding), snails, the
larvae of various open sea fishes and of course of fishes
inhabiting the weed, and many kinds of crustaceans in
their protective armour.

The ocean pipe-fish—a relation of the sea-horse and
having the same curious "horse's head" appearance—
is another inhabitant of the "sea garden". Pipe-fishes
have gills which are disposed in curious tufts on the
branchial arches: the gill-cover is a simple plate, and the
gill-aperture is very small. The attenuated body is covered
with bony plates. No ventral fins exist, and the jaws are
united to form a tube or pipe, bearing a small toothless
mouth at the tip—the fantastic mouth which gives the
fish its name. Its expression can be described as that of
a child pursing its lips in expectation of a kiss, or perhaps more accurately as that of a whistling school boy!

But the most remarkable feature of the pipe-fish,
strangely enough, is not its curious mouth but the pouch-
like fold possessed by the males of some species. This fold
is situated on the under side of the abdomen and
resembles the pouch of a kangaroo, not merely in appearance but in its purpose—for it carries the pipe-fish's
babies around for a little while after birth. The eggs
formed in the female fish are delivered into the male
fish's pouch. There they hatch out, after which he retains

them for a while and then permits them to have separate existences from their curious parents.

All the pipe-fishes are feeble swimmers, in fact their progress through the weeds might best be described as crawling rather than swimming. If greatly enlarged motion-pictures of them could be taken they would appear as horses, moving slowly through the jungle.

The king of the weed jungle is most certainly the Sargassum Fish—a monarch bearing the impressive Latin name of *Histrio histrio*. This extraordinary fish is a rapacious cannibal. He crawls on arm-like fins through the "undergrowth" like a fearsome monster of the land-surface jungles. He camouflages himself like a bunch of *Sargassum* weed—branches, leaves, bladders and all. His fore fins are modified into jointed armlike appendages like crab's claws. His face is one of the most frightening of all fishy countenances. He stalks his prey with the cunning of a cat. If fishes are indeed terrified by horrific monsters of their own element, then those which meet this crab-like, cat-like bunch of weed with its ghastly face must be paralysed with fright.

One explorer captured three of these gruesome creatures and kept them for a brief while in a running-water aquarium. A day or so passed and (after the fashion of the nigger-boys in the nursery rhyme) "then there were two". Another interval and there was only one. Another extraordinary fact about this fish is that it actually attracts its victims, after stalking them and petrifying them with its appearance, by dangling a fleshly bait (the remains of a previous meal) before its victim, jiggling it about to whet its victim's appetite, before suddenly pouncing and swallowing it.

Although the fishes which have been found in the Sargasso suggest that the varieties are nothing like as numerous as those of the open sea, yet those which do inhabit the Sargasso appear to be unusually strange kinds, justifying the weird legends associated with the vast whirlpool, not in supernatural manifestations but in natural phenomena. There is the marbled angler, for instance, a nightmarish animal which challenges the sargassum fish for frightfulness and is only (literally) beaten by a head: the sargassum fish's uglier death's-head.

The marbled angler is thick in proportion to its length —it is in fact fearsomely squat. Its main peculiarity is that the extremities of its fins and tail are like beautiful fronds of maidenhair. These waving fringes do not give the fish a graceful appearance. They only emphasize its ugliness and give the impression that the creature is a denizen of another world than our own.

Crabs, shrimps and prawns abound in the Sargasso, as also do many varieties of snails and mussels. There are numerous varieties of snails among the weeds, extraordinarily beautiful in colour and (according to epicures who have tasted them) far more delicious than land snails.

Some of the most curious facts regarding the "garden whirlpool" are those concerned with eels.

For untold centuries—probably since the world's first humans took to the seas in their primitive boats—men have disputed the details of the life-history of these wonderful creatures. They arrive as tiny wriggling shapes in our estuaries, swim up our rivers, and when fully matured return to the wide expanses of the ocean, where —until quite recent years—they have vanished: passing beyond human investigation.

It was the Danish zoologist, Johannes Schmidt (1877–1933), a naturalist who spent most of his life studying flatworms, sponges and other forms of marine life, who discovered that the eels of European rivers make journeys of incredible length through the waters to the Sargasso Sea, there to spawn and die after accomplishing their amazing mission. What mysterious instinct guides them through the trackless wastes, so that they do not wander and lose themselves but arrive, time after time, at their destination?

When eels are born they are such tiny threads, and so transparent, that they are practically invisible: only their minute eyes can be seen. They are lilliputian ghosts, hairs of living light, made from a substance more efficient in its optical qualities than lucite: the modern plastic which man uses for his aeroplane windows, reflectors and beautiful ornaments.

Great colonies of fresh-water eels spawn in the salt seas south of Bermuda, in close proximity to the Sargasso, according to the latest available evidence, but this does not mean that other swarms may not spawn within the gigantic wheel. All the evidence, old and new, shows that the mature eels have the Sargasso as their objective as they leave the rivers.

The vast jungle-growths of that area are distinguished from the surrounding sea by their rich, unexploited chemical products, such as iodine, chlorine, bromine and sulphur. Can it be that eels sense these chemicals, by the use of modifications in their nervous systems quite unknown to us?

All forms of migration in nature are mysterious and probably insoluble from any materialistic viewpoint.

Many ichthyologists have told the sensational story of the eel's travel-cycle. The elvers—baby eels—reach the coasts of Europe in autumn or winter, when they have grown to a length of about two inches. In many places along the European coasts they are caught with sieves, boiled in salted water, and eaten, usually with a sauce or vinegar. Those that escape penetrate the rivers into fresh water, where they seek and prefer an area of hard ground, rock or flint, to one of tangled seaweed: a remarkable practice in view of the fact that it involves a preference for surroundings so completely different from the *Sargassum* environment in which it was born. The change from salt to fresh water is but one of the drastic changes they have survived. They remain for three years near the mouths of the rivers, swelling and growing in length all the time. Then, while their thyroid glands are developing, they move farther and farther up the rivers, until they have attained a length of as much as three feet, and a weight up to thirteen pounds.

During their progress up the rivers there has been no differentiation in sex—they have been sexually undeveloped throughout the journey. At last—seven or eight years have elapsed since they left the Sargasso—they become distinct sexes.

They are now far up the rivers, and the males have become sexually mature, but (unlike salmon) the eels do not have their young there at journey's end. Why have they come so far—struggling through the waters of the ocean, resting awhile in the estuaries, and battling against the river's seaward currents to these places? As these are not their breeding grounds the driving impulse cannot be sexual.

But now—first to the males—comes the home-hunger which takes them all the long journey back again. Feeling the compelling force of the Sargasso call, the mature male eels leave their fresh-water homes high up in the rivers and swim back until they reach salt water again, plunging into it in their shining myriads and battling their way unerringly outward—farther and farther outward—through the ocean wastes until they reach their objective. There is no explanation of this apparently senseless separation of the males from the females at the very climax of their sexual development. For the females wait, back there up the rivers, not weeks or months but years, before following the males. They are between ten and fifteen years old before the Sargasso call comes to *them*. When the moment arrives they, too, go down the rivers, through the estuaries and out to the open sea—anything up to eight years later than the males who have preceded them.

After the voyage of the females, reunited near the Sargasso, the mature eels lose their appetites and their golden hues. While this is happening the sexual organs of the females—which have been organically perfect for years—develop excessively.

The eels have travelled at great depths to reach their spawning grounds, particularly in passing through the Straits of Gibraltar. They have taken about six months in their journeys—both males and females, with that wide interval between—from their temporary homes far up the rivers. During that time their eyes have developed into great lenses capable of piercing the turgid darkness of the deeps, while their skins have developed a brilliance amounting almost to luminescence, so that they have been able to keep together—each voyager's position known to the others, each migratory swarm intact. Only when they reach their spawning grounds do the eels rise to the surface, here, there and everywhere—each migrating colony adding its numbers to the swarming masses darting in and out of the weed fringes.

They now approach the climax of their existences. For this they have made the enormous two-way journey.

Having fertilized the females the males soon die, not long after their return to the Sargasso. But the females survive for several years more—some of them adding as much as ten years to their life-spans. They lay their eggs—averaging no fewer than five million from each mother-eel. But they do not lay them on the surface. The mother-eels go down into the depths to give them birth—down, down to an average depth of no less than three thousand two hundred and fifty feet: roughly *three-quarters of a mile* below the surface. Vastly increased pressures operate at that depth. The eggs spawned by the mother eels are barely a fifth of an inch in length, yet what *bathyscaphes* they must be, tougher than steel, to withstand such pressures! From the eggs tiny creatures emerge, bearing the lengthy name: "preleptocephali".

Lacking mouths, these larvae grow until they are twice the length of their egg-cases, but they are still only two-fifths of an inch long. Fifteen months have now elapsed since they were born, and they are still three-quarters of a mile below the surface. They are now termed "leptocephali" by man. The moment has arrived for them to rise through the 3,000-odd feet of water to the surface. Many have died down there in the icy currents. Why did the mothers go down, seeing that eels naturally love the warmer water? Science has no explanation. Why did migrating eels, in their long homeward journeys to the Sargasso, go down into the colder waters and the far greater pressures? Again, there is no explanation.

The leptocephali are now on the surface again, where they mingle with the plankton, and—with their mouths, which they have so miraculously developed—begin to feed voraciously. As they feed they penetrate outward from the Sargasso into the Gulf Stream, and are slowly swept by it towards the European coasts, so that one of the most remarkable life-cycles in all natural history begins all over again.

Is it all the work of blind chance? It surely requires more credulity than any observer possesses to believe that the entire complicated, ingenious process can be explained from any mechanistic, materialistic view-point.

In their long journeys from the Sargasso whirlpool across vast stretches of water to their mating-places high up in many of the world's rivers, and back again to their Sargasso breeding grounds, eels link distant reaches of the oceans with areas of the world's coastlines. We now journey with them in imagination, inward from the spinning whirlpools to the shores, to find new fields of fascinating interest awaiting us.

CHAPTER VII

COASTLINES

THE oceans of the world, waging incessant warfare against its land surfaces, meet the land areas along a series of twisting, receding, advancing coastlines which are not "no-man's-lands" of lifelessness and desolation, but thronged battlefields of infinitely-varied activity.

Such shore-lines, extending around the world, are (by reason of their complicated convolutions, their bays, promontories and irregularities generally) hundreds of thousands of miles in total length. Men have "walked around the world" but no human has ever contemplated the colossal task of walking around the world's coastlines. Such a journey would need many lifetimes.

Picturing the coastlines as a vast net, with great breaks and no regular meshes, or as a tangle of strings enveloping the earth, it must be appreciated that no section of the "string", however short, is without its teeming life. In any single square mile where sea and land meet, throughout the entire meshwork, countless myriads of creatures live and die. No one has ever attempted a census of them. Ignoring for a moment the creatures which live on the ocean surfaces, and the enormous number which live in its deeps, the tens of thousands of varieties of shore animals comprise a "coastal population" which must be millions of times greater than the world's human population.

From such an overwhelming multitude of living creatures we can select only a few typical specimens. The eyes of humans, aided by microscopes, behold only a tiny fraction of the coastline populations. Darwin realized that he could occupy several lifetimes in the study of earthworms. One would need as many to study the anatomy, habits and life-cycle of any single coastal species, selected at random from among the tens of thousands of distinct kinds which inhabit the world's sea-fringes.

The tides of the sea, conspiring with the world's rivers, continually deposit living animals and organic matter upon the ocean shores, but such living and (apparently) dead material is not left anywhere where it is deposited. The word "apparently" is a necessary qualification, for even the waste matter and debris deposited by waves on the shores, and by land and ocean rivers in their tidal interplay, swarm with microscopic life.

We must therefore begin our survey of the world's coasts with this basic conception: that they are not merely areas of rock formation, or stretches of sand and pebble, subject to breaking and receding rollers, but worlds within worlds of living creatures, and that the waters which beat against them and flow inward and outward across them are inhabited—every cubic inch of them—by untold millions of microscopic life-forms.

Corals in infinite variety, shells in almost inconceivable profusion, crustaceans of every imaginable kind, and enormous multitudes of fish, are here along the coastlines for our selective examination. Those that we consider will serve to illustrate the magic, beauty and wonderment of the multitudinous shapes which rest and move along the coasts, and float or swim in the waters that cover the ocean shelves.

There are three main divisions of the living creatures of the sea, if they are classified according to their life-habits. The term *nekton* comprises the swimmers—fishes of all kinds, squids, whales, and so on. *Plankton* may be described as including those free-swimming creatures which drift or wander with the tides and currents. The third division, *benthos*, comprises all those forms which crawl over or burrow into the sea-beds, and also those which are fixed in location, such as barnacles and sponges. But the sea will not be tamed—not even by man's classifications, so that even this "life-habit" classification is not definitive—the *nekton*, *plankton* and *benthos* compartments are by no means distinct, for numbers of creatures drift to and fro across the lines of demarcation as though the ocean itself was determined to erode or wash away arbitrary terminologies.

Even if we attempt a simpler division of sea creatures, into plants and animals, the ocean seems determined to mix them. For there are plant-like animals and animal-like plants. Plants often resemble animals so closely that it is difficult to distinguish them, while the same applies to animals which look like plants. There are seventeen hundred species of the *Bryozoa* alone. The name means "moss animals", and they are to be found in their myriads: moss-like and lichen-like creatures attached to the rocks, stones and pebbles of the world's sea-coasts; to pieces of seaweed and other natural growths, and to the shells of crabs, lobsters and other crustaceans.

The phrase "a fish out of water" is often used to describe a state of discomfort among incongruous or unnatural surroundings. It can, of course, be used with reference to the majority of fishes if any of them are taken out of their element, and even with regard to those which make occasional visits to the surface or brief flights above it: they cannot live out of the sea for long: they must soon die unless they return to the waters. Yet there are some sea creatures that seem anxious to get out of the water, and which live much of their lives away from it.

Among them are the mud-skippers, which inhabit the river mouths of various parts of Africa, Asia and Australia.

Other names given to the mud-skipper are "bommi", "walking-fish", and "jumping-fish", the scientific name is *Periophthalmus*—a reference to the fish's prominent eyes, which are set close together somewhat below the line of its profile, and are not only capable of protrusion and retraction, but are furnished with well-developed eyelids. The long body is covered with curious scales; the mouth-cleft is nearly horizontal, with the upper jaw protruding beyond the lower, while the teeth are conical and vertical—all this giving the fish a fatuous yet pugnacious expression. The first dorsal fin has a number of flexible spines, while the breast or pectoral fins are hand-like appendages. With these the creatures walk about over the mud-flats and climb on to the roots of mangrove trees and other forms of vegetation, where they will bask in the sunshine for hours at a time, dangling their tails in the water.

The mud-skipper has an excellent reason for this partial submersion of its tail. The tail is freely supplied with blood-vessels, and acts as a second respiratory organ which extracts air from the water—the fish takes in air from both ends. It is a matter of chance whether it breathes through the front end or both, but the fact that it has a habit of tossing itself into the air has nothing to do with this. It may be walking over the surface of the sand, hitching itself along about an inch at every "step", or "double step"—when suddenly one of its enemies may appear. It instantly becomes an expert acrobat. It curls its tail to one side and sharply straightens it out with a flick, therefore hurling itself upward and forward to a distance of three or four feet.

One species, *Periophthalmus schlosseri*, performs its antics along the shores of the Burmese rivers. At a distance they look like large tadpoles as they rest in the sun, occasionally snapping at flies or other passing insects. Suddenly they are startled by something, and off they go, each making its own hop, skip and jump across the mud, or perhaps leaping on to the water and skimming across it like a flat pebble thrown by a schoolboy.

Mud-skippers often climb trees, clinging to the rough bark until they reach a projecting stump or branch where they can perch and survey the strange world in which they live. While resting, a mud-skipper will often plant its "arms" firmly—using them as organs of support as a man places his elbows on the table.

The eyes of these creatures are most ingeniously devised. Not only can they be drawn in and pushed out: they can also be swivelled in all directions like the eyes of a chameleon. After death the mud-skipper's eyes sink to the level of the surrounding scales, losing their characteristic prominence.

It is believed that these fish have been driven from the sea by their numerous marine foes: the unpalatable nature of their flesh giving them some measure of protection from land animals.

The name "walking-fish" is shared by some of their near relatives, particularly the serpent-head, a fish of the East Indian and African genus, *Ophiocephalus*. These are able to live for long periods out of water, as they travel by wriggling through moist grass from one pool to another. They are from two to three feet long, and are covered with medium-sized scales—those on the flattened head being plate-like. Some thirty species of serpent-heads alone are known to us, inhabiting many parts of Asia; the commonest being a species which is sometimes found in a torpid condition in dried-up pools, as though the water had evaporated while the fish dozed —too lazy to find a better resting-place.

When living in muddy water, these fishes are compelled to rise to the surface at intervals or they die—they are not so acclimatized to the shores as the mud-skippers.

The serpent-head or snake-fish breathes atmospheric air instead of that dissolved in water; although, as we have seen, the mud-skipper takes in both kinds: from the atmosphere into its gill-chambers, and from the water through its partly-submerged tail. Unlike the mud-skipper (which can survive for as long as thirty-six hours out of water if it submerges its tail at intervals, but only for half that time if it breathes through its gills alone) the serpent-head has no rigid time limit for remaining on land, provided it has access to moisture in grass. It seems to have adapted itself to gill-breathing of atmospheric air without discomfort.

The climbing-fish, or climbing perch, is another fish which can remain for long periods on the shore. It is a spiny-rayed fish, and is characterized by the enlarged and peculiarly labyrinthine structure of its superior pharyngeal bones—those of the cleft, or cavity, forming the upper part of the gullet. These bones are wonderfully formed of infinitely delicate plates, enclosing the air-spaces between them in a microscopically complex mesh.

This labyrinthine organ is also found in other fishes, but is far more elaborately developed in the climbing perch, in which it serves as a breathing organ of incredible complexity and efficiency. To a fish like the climbing perch, which inhabits small stagnant pools (where the water contains only a small amount of dissolved air) when not climbing, such an apparatus is indispensable, for the creature breathes free air regularly like any land animal with lungs. Its habit of leaving the water and climbing trees is an extraordinary one which usually occurs during rains, when it will ascend the trunks of palm-trees to a height of six or eight feet, to catch insects. The habit is so well known to the natives of the West Indies that the animal has been known to them as "the fish that climbs trees" from time immemorial; but the stories were regarded as travellers' tales until quite recent times.

The truth of the story was finally established by the

German explorer Lieutenant Daldorf some years ago, when he was fortunate enough to observe one of the fish making its way up the trunk of a Palmyra palm. Since then many naturalists and other observers have witnessed to the truth of the fact that fishes *do* climb trees.

The late Dr. Nelson Annandale, of the Indian Museum in Calcutta, described another climbing-fish, which often hitches its way up the supporting posts of wooden houses built over the shore-waters of lakes, in the following words: "This little fish moves slowly up the post, browsing on encrusting plants and animals. It seems to use its tail in climbing, after a fashion which recalls the woodpecker's way of pressing its stiff tail-feathers against the roughness of the tree-stem. When the little fish wishes to rest on its ascent, it takes a firm hold with its lips."

An official of the Madras Fisheries once trained some climbing-fish to ascend a nearly vertical sheet of cloth dipped into the water of the aquarium in which they lived. Indian jugglers sometimes use the snake-head in their performances: the antics of the fish being calculated to preserve their reputations as "miracle men" and amuse their audiences.

There are other authentic descriptions of the way fish climb trees, in addition to the one given by Dr. Annandale. It is now certain that such fishes make use of their gill-covers, besides their spiny anal fins and tails, in making their ascents. These gill-covers are peculiarly constructed, so that each opercular bone has a serrated edge, which clings tenaciously to surfaces yet can be instantaneously released: a perfect device for its purpose. It works like a leg, being first extended by certain muscles and attached to the tree, and then (after the fish's body has been raised a little) the other parts of the fish take hold and the opercular bone is released, ready for attachment again.

This is an extraordinary instance of the use of an

organ designed for one purpose being used for a completely different one: the gill-cover made for breathing being employed for climbing!

The majority of fishes are egg-laying creatures. But a comparative few are viviparous—that is, their babies are born alive and not hatched from eggs previously formed and shed by their mothers. Among these few, some of the most notable are the viviparous blennies (*Zoarces viviparus*), one or two kinds of dogfish, most of the sharks, and the sawfish.

The blennies are small fishes—the largest, *Blennius gattorugine*, may grow to a foot in length, but this is exceptional—of which some forty species are found in the northern seas, the tropical Atlantic, the coasts of Tasmania, the Red Sea, and along the coasts and shallows in most parts of the world. Their elongated bodies, some of which are scaleless, are remarkable for the abundance of slimy matter with which they are covered. It is also remarkable for the fact that it possesses only one dorsal fin, which in some species is deeply divided, and for the way the coastal varieties use their ventral fins as "feet" to enable them to climb about among the rocks and seaweed of the shore.

The blennies depend upon crustaceans for their main food. If they are stranded on the shore by the ebb of the tide they can subsist for many hours, although their out-of-water endurance is nothing like that of the serpent-head. Some species, however, have adapted themselves to fresh water. Among these is the *Blennius vulgaris*, which inhabits inland lakes in Southern Europe. Blennies like to attach themselves to floating objects—coastal varieties have been found far out at sea clinging to "rafts" of one kind or another—while they will often deposit their eggs in strange places and keep watch over them afterwards. One species—which is not viviparous—has been known to lay its eggs inside a bottle cast up on the shore, get into the bottle itself, float away with it, and when dredged up by a net be found inside its buoyant glass nursery jealously guarding its babies!

The viviparous blennies produce small fry at birth which are perfectly transparent, and which are so fully developed as they leave their mothers that they can swim about freely. The mother blenny will give birth to from two to three hundred at a time; these distending her body so much that when they are ready to emerge (invariably head first) they may be extruded by the slightest pressure on her body.

The butterfish is a blenny, although its body is usually long and flattened from side to side. It guards its eggs—not being viviparous—by coiling itself completely around them, as it lies compressed into a ball in a hole or empty shell—almost like a cat curled up around her kittens. Because of its small head and fringe of fins the butterfish is sometimes mistaken for a young eel, but it is nearly twice as long (about six inches) as the elvers which swarm up our estuaries at certain times.

The butterfish has other picturesque names. The two best varieties in American waters are found along America's Atlantic coasts. One is the dollar-fish of the coasts of New York, Massachusetts and Maine. Others are the sheeps-head of Cape Cod, the pumpkin-seed of Connecticut, and the starfish of the Norfolk coasts. Some of these fish swim in company with large jelly-fishes, which protect them from other fishes. But jelly-fishes are the sea's gangsters, with their "stick-'em-up" streamers, threatening other forms of life, so that it is not to be wondered at that their "protection" of butterfishes often results in the latter getting "stung", and eventually "liquidated" in return for their misplaced confidence.

The harvest-fish, however, is one of the butterfish which seems to enjoy special immunity. It is found from Cape Cod southward to Brazil, but is more abundant about the mouth of Chesapeake Bay, where it is called "whiting". It is a delicious little fish for the frying-pan:

about six inches long in the Chesapeake Bay district, although it may be as long as ten inches in others. The "gangster" with which it associates is the Al Capone of all jelly-fish: that most fantastic many-individuals-in-one creature so studiously avoided by swimmers and known to mariners as the Portuguese man-of-war.

This extraordinary creature (or, more exactly, colony of creatures) belongs to that enormous group of life-forms known as the *Coelenterata*, ranking next above the sponges and their relatives in the ascending order of the animal scale, yet contrasting strongly with them. The creatures of the group are distinguished from those in other groups by the fact that each individual has a central digestive cavity, communicating with a system of canals, while it has prehensile organs around its mouth. The *Coelenterata* include corals, sea-firs, sea-pens, sea-anemones and jelly-fish—to give but a brief and inadequate list. The range of species within the group is vast and varied, ranging from tiny animals scarcely visible to the naked eye to monsters several feet across.

There are innumerable soft-bodied forms in the *Coelenterata*, composed almost entirely of water. There are—at the other extreme—the reef-builders, almost a hundred per cent limestone. There are species which burrow in the mud and trail tentacles, and (again going to the extreme) grotesque shapes like the Portuguese man-of-war—gangster-like "protector" of the American harvest-fish—floating on the surface and trailing their tentacles a little below it. But whatever their form, nearly all the Coelenterates—small, large, soft, hard, mud-burrowing or surface-floating—possess nematocysts: small stinging cells.

There have been many philosophic mariners through the centuries who have believed that every conceivable device found on land has its counterpart somewhere in the world's oceans, and writers of sea books have often shown tendencies to agree with the "old salts" in their speculations. Certainly one could make out a case for the belief by instancing contrivance after contrivance—and even creature after creature—on the world's land surfaces which are foreshadowed or duplicated in the oceans or along their coastlines. In many ways the world of dry land is one which is reflected in the world of waters.

The stinging cells of certain land organisms, such as nettles and thistles, are matched by the stinging cells of the Coelenterates. There is, superficially, nothing extraordinary about the resemblance. It seems quite natural and reasonable that stinging cells should be found both in the sea and on the land, as protective devices. The Portuguese man-of-war is not a duplication of a land creature, but a weird and sensational caricature of something made on land and launched by man into the sea, something indicated in its name: *a ship*.

It is a singularly beautiful creature, despite its almost nightmare-like grotesqueness. It is usually found floating—sometimes singly but usually in "fleets"—in tropical seas, but in the latter part of the summer it is often seen off the coast of New England. It is a jelly-fish of the genus *Physalia*, but any such brief and conventional description does the man-of-war injustice. In all the realm of nature there is no creature more curious and fascinating.

Bearing the likeness of a ship, it might more accurately be described as an armada. For it comprises the parts and features of many ships. It is less like a single life-form than a community, yet all the "individuals" which compose it are united in an organism which moves *as one* and lives with a common mysterious purpose. It can be called a "ship", and it has a crew—yet it has no captain. It is less like a democracy than a totalitarian state—save that it has no dictator: the "citizens" act as one, yet no individual controls them. Each man-of-war is a lovely vessel of rose, blue, purple and gold. It is a rainbow-hued, bladder-like float, which bobs about on the surface of the waves. From its "hull" masses of multi-coloured streamers descend below the surface. These may be as much as fifty feet long, and though they look harmless enough they are stinging tentacles.

The "hull" or "float" is a bag, sometimes a foot long, filled with gas which serves to keep the colony on the surface. By contracting itself it can discharge some of the gas, so that it can sink a little below the surface; or it can expel most of its gas through a pore (or "valve") enabling it to submerge completely.

The streamers, or tentacles, have various duties. Contrary to many superficial descriptions of the man-of-war, they are not all stinging tentacles: in fact only a few of them, comparatively, have stinging contrivances. Those which serve as "marines" or "guards" are so armed, and these have lasso-like devices which cling tightly around their prey and draw it towards a number of squirming siphons. Thousands of stinging barbs have been released —as though the "ship" had fired numerous torpedoes— which poison the victim and render it helpless. The mouths are sticky and cling to the prey on all sides, until it is at last enclosed, as though in a tight bag. It is then digested and carried into the stomachs of the siphons.

The stinging barbs need special mention. Each barb— and the "ship" carries thousands of them on its fighting tentacles—resembles an inverted tube, coiled up like a spring in a microscopically small box, which is covered by a lid. Attached to each box is a trigger-hair. Immediately this is touched it is stimulated chemically: the lid flies open and the inverted tube within the box shoots out with lightning-like rapidity, turning inside out as it flies, and so exposing the vicious, pointed spines which had been concealed in the inverted form of the tube. Imagine the finger of a glove, with spikes on the outside. Turn it inside-out and you have the spikes pointing inwards—the position of the stinging barbs before release.

Imagine the glove-finger instantaneously restored to its normal position, and you have the action which takes place as the tiny tubes shoot out. The tiny thread-like barbs can be used only once. After they are discharged they are replaced with new ones.

We have seen that the barbs are released by triggers which operate when stimulated in *two* ways—by contact and by chemical action. The most extraordinary fact about the man-of-war is that the process is not strictly automatic. For the fishes which swim in and out among the tentacles, and are apparently given permission to do so by the man-of-war, continually brush against the triggers—yet they are not released. This implies that the man-of-war has some kind of control over the chemical stimuli of the triggers and can restrain their action.

Besides its "fighting units", the man-of-war has "individuals" which perform very different duties. Some are flask-shaped bodies which do nothing but eat. Others, resembling clusters of small berries, are continually occupied in producing more and more eggs, to develop into more and more "ships" for the "fleet". Other organisms are solely occupied in repairing any damage caused to the "vessel". There are also organisms which control the man-of-war's speed and direction.

The man-of-war is a "ship" that sails—propelled by wind-power. It has a huge float (the "sail") extending along its upper surface. The "hull" itself is much larger and blunter at the stern, to which all the tentacles and organisms of the "ship" are attached, leaving the "bow" free to force its way through the water. The sail has a shell-like appearance. The course of the "ship" is steered by the longest tentacles—which lie outside the others. They serve as living rudders, for they trail backward as the vessel moves, acting as a controllable "brake" or "drag" on the vessel's movement. If the wind impelling the vessel forward is too strong, the rudder-like streamers are lengthened considerably, reducing its speed. If there is only a light wind then the streamers are shortened so that there is little or no "drag" and the vessel gets the utmost benefit from the available wind.

To alter the vessel's course, the streamers change both size and position. Those on the starboard side may shorten and adjust themselves to the "ship" so that it can turn to port, either sharply or slowly—and vice versa. The streamers can also prevent lateral drift and keep the vessel on a steady course. Lengthened considerably they can make the vessel "heave to" and "anchor," even in mid-ocean.

One investigator of the man-of-war's extraordinary habits, took one of the creatures—holding it by a special device, to prevent it stinging him—and lowered it slowly into a bucket. As he did so the streamers—touching the bottom of the bucket—shortened and shortened, until they were only a fraction of their original length.

The man-of-war does not attempt to control its movements when the surface of the sea is too rough—it allows itself to drift with the wind and tide, so that it is sometimes cast up on beaches. Bathers who have come across the dead bodies of these creatures have often learned, too late to prevent acute discomfort, that even after the "vessel" itself is dead, the "fighting units" may still live on—releasing their poisonous barbs when contacted.

There have been cases of people killed by the man-of-war. One of the most recent was a strong and healthy young Filipino, nineteen years old, who was gathering firewood while working waist-deep in the water of a Philippine Island mangrove swamp a year or so ago. He was stung by a man-of-war concealed in the waters. His fellow-workers rushed him to the shore and he was examined by Dr. H. W. Wade, Chief Pathologist of the near-by Culion Leper Colony. The only mark on his body was a purplish discoloration encircling his right knee. Dr. Wade concluded that he had died from drowning, through being rendered helpless by the stings.

Several years before this, Dr. E. H. H. Old, in the *Philippine Journal of Science*, reported the death of a boy of fourteen,. who was stung by a man-of-war and died in a state of hysteria.

There are many other jelly-fish which are harmful, and some of these resemble the man-of-war, although none possess all its fighting and sailing qualities. There is, for instance, the *Velella* jelly-fish, which is very abundant in tropical waters, and may often be found washed up in its thousands on the Florida beaches. It is sometimes confused with the man-of-war, for it also has a raft-like float, but it is quite distinct in shape, being long and flattened, while it is vividly blue in colour.

Apart from the fact that both the man-of-war and the *Velella* have floats there is little resemblance between them. The man-of-war's tentacles, as we have seen, are capable of extension to fifty feet, but the *Velella's* are short and thread-like, while the animal (or "polyperson", to use its more accurate name) has a "hull" which is divided into watertight compartments, which is an advance on the man-of-war's one-compartment structure. Another striking difference is that the *Velella* has a well-developed triangular sail placed diagonally across it.

Despite the fact that the *Velella* is an abundant and widespread polyperson, scientists know little about it. Yet from the time of Haeckel, who studied the *Hydromedusae* exhaustively, an enormous amount of human research has gone into the investigation of the anatomy and habits of this group of marine animals. There are vast varieties of them, and even the single order of *Siphonophora*, to which the man-of-war and *Velella* belong, has so many differentiated kinds, some of which merge into each other, while numbers of them present problems of classification, that scientists cannot agree among themselves in their theories regarding the life-cycles and anatomical devices of numerous members of the group. Many jelly-fishes, in fact, which are much simpler in their structures than the *Siphonophores*, are still baffling scientific explanation, while of the origins and habits of some of them scientists know little or nothing.

New and hitherto unknown species of jelly-fish may appear suddenly along a particular section of coastline. The animals may simply swarm in the sea and be washed ashore in great numbers. Then, with similar suddenness, they will vanish as mysteriously as they appeared. Whence they come and whither they go no one knows. Sometimes they will reappear after a lapse of many years; sometimes a completely new species will come out of the sea, disappear into it again, and be seen no more.

Nor are they always tiny creatures which may have been overlooked on past occasions: some of the creatures performing the appearing-disappearing act may be several feet in diameter. But whether they are produced by monstrous hydroidal forms completely unknown to us, moving in the depths of the sea, or are the offspring of other free-swimming *Medusae* in the surface waters, no one knows.

To many people the word "jelly-fish" conjures up a picture of a sea creature of fairly simple construction: the average person has seen a few forms at the seaside or in aquaria and has no conception of their stupendous variety and vast differences in structure. Fortunately, the jelly-fish most frequently found along British shores are quite harmless. It is not unusual in summer to see numbers of them stranded on flat sandy beaches, by the combined action of tide and onshore wind. Or you may go for a row on a warm and sunny day and glimpse many of the *Aurelia* (the jelly-fish most common to our coasts) drifting lazily just below the surface. Those stranded on the beach may appear flabby, nasty-looking objects: those seen over the side of the boat look very different—colourful, graceful, like flowers of the sea. But in neither case do the jelly-fish seem extraordinary.

You may examine a specimen left in a pool on the shore, probably the handsome *Aurelia aurita*, with its four violet loops clearly visible within its almost transparent body. The loops are the creature's organs of reproduction, but its anatomy, habits and life story seem commonplace enough compared with those of the man-of-war, so that *Aurelia aurita* seems a creature of this world, and the man-of-war a monster from another—yet they are close relatives among the myriads of living creatures which throng the world's shores and coastal waters.

Nothing in nature is commonplace. Darwin, who spent years of his life studying the earthworm, confessed that he knew very little about it. Lubbock devoted most of his life to the study of ants, bees and wasps, yet frankly admitted his ignorance of them. The life story of the *Aurelia aurita* is simply told. But it is only superficially simple. You might spend a lifetime studying it and still— like Darwin and the earthworm—know very little about it.

It is typical of the life stories of numerous jelly-fishes. The creatures are male and female, but their breeding process superficially seems more plant-like than that of other members of the animal kingdom.

The male jelly-fish release their sperm into the water, and the females, swimming nearby, contact it and are fertilized. The mother *Aurelia aurita* is much more devoted to her babies than most jelly-fish: she retains her tiny eggs in a membraneous "pocket" until they hatch out. They have no resemblance to their parents as they drift about and eventually fasten themselves to rocks on the sea-bed near the shore. Time passes and each infant gradually assumes the appearance of a tiny sea-anemone with a mouth that never closes, and four rudimentary tentacles grouped around it. These lengthen and increase in number until it possesses thirty-two writhing feelers. Side-shoots are then developed until the creature looks more like a vegetable than an animal, and remains like this for several years—as though nature had made a mistake and the creature was destined to end its life as a carnivorous underwater plant, quite unlike its parents.

But at last the "plant" begins to throw off dozens of small transparent discs, none of them as large as rain-drops. Each of these is a freely-swimming jelly-fish, complete with a fringe of microscopic tentacles—a tiny disc that pulsates rhythmically as it swims.

Most of the larger jelly-fish are the medusa-stage of the Coelenterate class *Scyphozoa*. Our description of the life-cycle of one applies to one species of *Aurelia*, but there are *Aurelia* of many kinds and sizes. There is, for instance, the large jelly-fish common to the coast of New England, *Aurelia flavidula*, which sometimes reaches a diameter of ten inches. All the *Aurelia* are miniature umbrellas, but the *Aurelia flavidula* is one of the ornate ones, with ornamental additions of its own. Its convex body is smooth on its upper surface, while four thick lobes hang from it which unite to form the creature's mouth, also giving off four tentacles. The margin of the "umbrella" is fringed and carries eight eyes, each covered by a lobe. Just under the surface are the water-vascular canals, radiating from the stomach. When in motion, the entire "umbrella" contracts and expands rhythmically at an average rate of twelve to fifteen pulsations a minute.

A less common jelly-fish on the coast of New England and in some parts of the North Atlantic is the monstrous *Cyanea arctica*, or "blue jelly", which sometimes grows to three or four feet in diameter, and has long tentacles (sometimes extending to 100 feet) filled with stinging lasso-cells which are poisonous to fishermen and bathers. In exceptional circumstances the *Aurelia* do not pass through the intermediate "plant-like" stage, but develop their true jelly-fish characteristics more directly. The *Hydrozoa* are more numerous in tropical seas, where they comprise forms of extraordinary beauty and coloration.

Scientists find it extremely difficult to make cut-and-dried classifications of the habitats of the creatures of the sea. The lower deeps merge into the middle deeps and these into the surface waters, while these again blend with the waters over the continental shelves, which yet again pass without rigid demarcation lines into the borders of the sea: its shallows and shore-edges. So with the creatures themselves, for classifications tend to be arbitrary, and the countless species, from the lowest forms up to sea-mammals merge together with imperceptible graduations, like the colours of a rainbow.

There is one region which can be treated as a sharply defined area, capable of simpler classification: the shore between tide-marks. In this area the conditions of life are unique, so that it is to be expected that the plants and animals inhabiting the area will not be found elsewhere. Jelly-fish are, in a sense, invaders of this clearly defined area—they are stranded upon it rather than inhabitants of it.

Shore life presents animals and plants with peculiar problems. These are mainly due to the fluctuating conditions obtaining between tide-marks. Covered and uncovered twice every twenty-four hours, by the ebb and flow of the tide, the shore creatures live surrounded or lapped by sea water when the tide is in, and subjected to the influence of the local climate with its air conditions when the tide is out. Rocks on the shore often become extremely hot—even hotter than the air above them—as when some rocks near Plymouth, England, during a recent summer, showed a temperature of 120 degrees, too hot for human feet. Yet sea creatures such as limpets and barnacles on the rock, which had been chilled by the sea some hours before, were alive and well. Rain is another challenge to the hardihood of intertidal animals and plants.

As a general rule—although a few creatures like eels and salmon are the exceptions—land forms die when submerged in water (salt or fresh) while aquatic forms of many kinds cannot survive dry land conditions. Yet the numerous plants and animals between tide-marks survive drastic changes without ill effects. They are deprived of their watery medium as the tide recedes, when they are exposed to the air, the heat of the sun and sometimes fresh water due to the rain.

The pounding of the waves on the world's sea-shores has affected the general shape of all plants and animals in the intertidal areas. Most of the creatures which live fully exposed to the action of the waves have been flattened down from above: crabs, starfish, etc. But there are some which are flattened laterally, such as sand-hoppers: they "lie down" to the sea's merciless blows. Limpets living in sheltered crevices are rounded. Those which live in exposed places are oval and flattened.

Myriads of creatures resist the sea's tearing and driving percussions by burrowing in the beaches, or clinging tenaciously to rocks—yet there are always a number that get carried away and swirled about in the waters. Shore creatures cling to rocks in all kinds of ways. Most molluscs hold on, by suction, by adapting their muscular "feet" to every microscopical roughness of the rock's surface. But the mollusc evidently finds that this is not enough, for it uses the edge of its shell like a file and works it a little way into the surface of the rock to get a firmer hold. The anemone is unable to supplement its hold with the rasping action, so it presses its body so closely to the rock that its flesh is adapted to every minute indentation over as wide an area as possible. The common barnacle cements itself to the rock with a secretion which securely fixes the box in which it lives to the surface of its dwelling-place.

Mussels hold on by their beards. Each beard—technically called the "byssus"—is a cluster of brown threads. Each thread is furnished with a terminal device, something like the ones used by creepers to attach themselves to garden walls or the walls of houses. A gland within the substance of the mussel's "foot" produces the material for the threads, and it issues in a thick fluid which runs along a groove extending down the hinder surface of the "foot", which plants the threads wherever they are required.

The threads are arranged with consummate skill, first in one direction then in another, the fluid running along the groove and spreading out into a rounded disc at the point where it touches the rock. There it becomes a terminal sucker, at the end of an extremely strong thread, which has been formed by the hardening of the fluid. When the fastening operation is complete the mussel is held in position by a mass of threads which diverge from it like the guide-ropes of a tent—and no tent ever erected by man was ever put up more efficiently. The threads are directed forwards, so that (unless the mussel is tightly packed in with others) the animal is able to swing round slightly, with its narrower end facing the force of the sea, thus enabling it to resist wave action from any direction. If the threads are broken the mollusc forms new ones readily, and can move about for a while before attaching itself again—it can even raise itself above mud and sediment.

Mussels live on plankton, which they strain out of the water that continually passes through their gill-plates, which are enormously enlarged in proportion to their size. The muscular power of mussels is amazing. When one closes its shell tightly it uses force equivalent to lifting 132 times its own weight.

Eider ducks are very fond of shellfish. As they are feeding it may happen that one of them will pick up a mussel in such a way that the animal will close its shells firmly on the bird's beak or tongue. Holding on like grim death the mussel may be fixed in such a manner that it cannot be swallowed, or broken against the rocks. If the bird tried to rid itself by dipping its beak in salt water the action would have no effect on the mussel—it would continue to cling tenaciously. Who has taught the eider (which is a sea creature) the only way to release itself from the mussel's grip? For there is only one way, and this the eider takes. The bird is a sea-living creature, and rarely except in the breeding season does it visit fresh water. Yet if it gets a mussel clamped tightly on its beak it will get away from the sea to the nearest stretch of fresh water. There it will keep ducking its head: for the mussel, which thrives in salt water, is killed by fresh water.

So rich are the beds of mussels in many parts that it is not thought necessary to cultivate them, although experiments on the Lancashire coast and elsewhere have shown that small, stunted mussels from overcrowded areas grow to large marketable ones if transplanted to other areas.

On the west coast of France, in the shallow bay called Anse de L'Aiguillon, they have been cultivated for centuries. The system of breeding them goes back over seven hundred years to the time when an Irishman named Walton, voyaging in a small ship carrying sheep, was wrecked there, in 1235. He and the sheep were the only survivors, and in trying to catch fish he discovered that mussels covered his nets thickly because the nets were raised above the mud, in which they would other-wise have been smothered. Walton then began the method of cultivation which has been carried on ever since—using twigs fastened to stakes, to which the mussels attach themselves. This is the "bouchot" system —the boucholeurs pushing themselves out to the bou-chots (stakes) in flat-bottomed boats with the help of one foot encased in a large sea boot and swung over the side of the boat.

Mussels are no friends of oysters. They menace them in a curious way, sometimes literally smothering oyster beds with their accumulated masses, which bury the oysters alive in a rock-like tomb.

Many creatures of the shore which seem stationary have some power of movement. The sea-urchin and the starfish, with their myriads of tube-like feet (somewhat resembling the rubber "dummies" with which Victorian mothers pacified their babies) are almost agile animals as they move from place to place. When compelled to do so, the limpet can move house by simply walking away with it. But all these ambulatory exercises are limited in area and most encrusting animals cannot do otherwise than "stay put". If danger threatens them, all they can do is to "shut the door" and hope for the best.

But the common barnacle does better than this—it takes a supply of air into its house before locking up. It is a tiny crustacean which, when the tide is in, stands *upside-down* in its box-like dwelling, which is made of plates of lime, and switches food towards itself with its slender legs. The tide recedes, and it shuts the doors—four of them, which are tightly-fitting valves. But as it does so it is careful to entrap a bubble of air and also sufficient moisture to keep its gills damp.

When you are walking along the shore, just after the tide has turned from the rocks, you may hear (all around you, if there are sufficient barnacles in the area) the "whispering" of the little creatures: a faint crackling sound. You may have precipitated it by the vibrations of your walking feet. The sound comes from the closing of countless thousands of those doors in the tiny houses, combined with the rupture of the air-bubbles as the barnacles make themselves snug. Sealed in their homes, they may remain shut up for days or weeks, not taking any food and conserving the air by "breathing" hardly at all.

We cannot leave the armoured hosts of the sea-shore without hearing what the oyster has to tell us about itself, although its name has become proverbially associated with reticence. It is an amazingly prolific creature. For instance, the American oyster may produce hundreds of millions of eggs in its lifetime. Near the oyster grounds the sea may be literally crowded with myriads of free-swimming larvae, which, when they settle on any hard surface available, may entirely cover it with tiny oysters (each smaller than a pin's head). Observers have counted as many as 1,000 oysters on a single square inch of hard surface: they may be compared with the star-dust of the sky for numbers. One remarkable fact at once emerges—all the tiny creatures lie on their left sides.

As they spend their lives in their beds they must have their food brought to them. The sea obliges them, taking them microscopic food of all kinds—minute plant life, the bacteria of decaying plants, food in abundance, for oysters' ancestors have chosen their resting-places well: estuaries rich in edible organisms. They have their regular feeding times, and the food is intercepted by the tiny oysters' gills and filtered out as the sea water passes through them, and digested in their gut.

There are various kinds of oysters, but we will first consider the American variety (*Ostrea virginica*). The female delivers her eggs—about fifty million at a time—into the sea. They float: the male has already released his sperm, which fertilizes them. He is very casual and un-concerned—only a few of the eggs may be fertilized. The rest die—but more than enough have begun their strange life-cycles.

We now turn to the European oyster (*Ostrea edulis*). The female lays only a hundredth of the number of eggs produced by the American oyster—about fifty thousand at a time—but their chances of survival are more than compensated by parental care. For after they have been fertilized *within the shell of the mother* with sperm collected by her from the water, the little ones swim around, im-prisoned, until she is ready to release them. She literally shoots them out like shots from a blunderbuss when they are about a fortnight old. They now swim freely in the sea and find their own food. After ten days of this free existence they sink to the sea-bed, or on to the netting, brush or lattice-work provided by man as he prepares to take advantage of their forthcoming change to a state of immobility.

Oysters are distributed as the result of their free existence in infancy, for drifting spat (as the larvae are called) may travel long distances. No one knows how long oysters may live if undisturbed. Some authorities say they can live for as long as thirty years. But when artificially reared they are allowed only four or five years of life before being collected for human consumption.

The oyster is a highly developed creature. It has a liver, intestines, and a heart with a blood-circulating system (although the blood is colourless) and it even has a complicated nervous system and a brain. None of these organs resemble our own, but they are as described. Although the common scallop has eyes—a hundred of them, each with its lens, retina and optic nerve—the oyster is eyeless. Its enemies include rays, starfish, boring sponges, certain marine leeches, octopuses, and those most deadly foes of the oyster the bloodthirsty insatiable Dog whelks and oyster tingles.

Although these are burdened with a heavy shell they roam about seeking whom they may devour. They are ruthless housebreakers and nature has obligingly provided them with a file, to rasp its way *into* the shells of other organisms. The file is called a radula, and is a ribbon of closely-set teeth.

The surf-scoter, a bird that lives in the northern oceans, is not provided with a beak suitable for opening oyster-shells, so it simply swallows them whole. They open inside the bird's gizzard, in which plenty of stones are lodged to grind the shells to pieces.

In Jamaica the lower branches of mangrove trees are often covered by water at high tide. Oysters suspend themselves from the branches, so that it would be true to say that they "grow on trees" in that country.

Oysters die strange deaths. One of the most curious is when their own descendants pile upon them in such prodigious numbers as they lie on the sea-bed that those underneath are stifled in their enforced imprisonment.

Of the innumerable battles which take place incessantly in shore waters, the struggle which ensues when a starfish attacks an oyster is one of the most remarkable. The starfish opens the attack by straddling the oyster and attaching its feet to the upper valve of its shell-case. It tugs and tugs at the upper shell, using all its strength against the oyster, who tries desperately to keep its door shut against the marauder. Eventually, no matter how long the struggle, the starfish wins the unequal battle. The oyster shell-case is forced open and the starfish turns its own stomach inside-out and forces it into the shell. In that position, with the stomach inside-out and the oyster helpless, the contents of the shell-case are quickly absorbed and digested. The starfish crawls away at last, having withdrawn its stomach, leaving the empty shell.

For every curious or pretty shell, preserved in someone's home, countless millions lie crushed and broken on the shores of the world, or pressed down by the weight of the waters, on the sea-beds. Yet every shell was once the armour of a living creature which was born wrapped in a transparent mantle of singular beauty. Each mantle has the power of extracting lime from sea water, which it builds up into the creature's adult shell, usually colouring it with rainbow-like hues in the process.

This wonderful mantle which nature has given to the *Mollusca*—the name means "soft-bodied"—may be seen in any common animal that wears a shell, such as the oyster or periwinkle. The way the mantle builds up the protective armour is instanced in the periwinkle's development. When it was very small it was no larger than a pin's head. As its body grew it needed a larger home. So the creature pushed some of its soft mantle out of the aperture of its shell, where it spread out a little and shell material deposited, forming a larger extension of the first shell, which was only a tiny transparent bead. So the building process went on, each extension of the shell being larger and generally thicker as more and more shell material was laid down.

The varied shapes of sea-shells are all built in this way: the creatures within them having their own inherited "blue-prints" of the houses they patiently build. Molluscs with heads, like the periwinkle, the snail and the whelk, have their mantle all in one piece and so grow single or univalve shells. The oyster (like other headless molluscs) lays down separate shells with each half of its mantle, so that it becomes a bivalve.

The periwinkle, like the whelk, has its own rasp, which it uses to scrape pieces off the seaweed it passes over, leaving tiny indentations in the weed as it goes. The rasp wears away, but the periwinkle has its own method of replacing the worn section. If you could look into its mouth you would find the lower part paved with sharp teeth, as though a number of tiny nails had been driven into it, with their points outwards. This rasp—sometimes called a tongue, though *radula* is the more appropriate name—is only the end of a strap (often two and a half inches long) furnished with six hundred rows of teeth, three in each row, which is coiled up in a fold of the periwinkle's body. Its edges are folded together at the back of the animal's mouth, and from that point it goes backward, folded, as a reserve of gristly, spiked strap. As the front portion becomes worn so it is broken off and the back portion feeds in to the periwinkle's mouth, furnished with new teeth, ready-sharpened for use.

Shelled sea creatures may be said to live within their skeletons: the hard parts of their bodies which form a protecting armour, properly described an exoskeleton. But there are many different kinds of structure and material used by Nature to support and protect the softer and more vulnerable parts of inhabitants of the sea, and among them all there are none more ingenious and remarkable than the skeletons of sponges.

Almost all of these are supported by loose or firmly fused spicules of lime or silica, or (as in the case of the common bath sponge) "over-all" skeletons consisting of interwoven horny fibres.

Occurring in great profusion, from the shores of many countries outwards and downwards into the great deeps, sponges are such curious animals, in their manifold structures and strange habits, that they remained insoluble puzzles for centuries. In early times they were thought to be "worm-nests"; in later centuries they were classed with seaweeds; and it was not until a little over a century ago that our real knowledge of them began. Even today they remain baffling and mysterious—life-forms which are among the queerest of all the extraordinary creatures to be found in the world's oceans.

E*

CHAPTER VIII

SPONGES AND CORALS

WHEN men put on diving-suits, or use similar devices to descend into the sea, they are immediately aware of the fact that many underwater animals seem to accept them as creatures not unlike themselves. Some creatures show a little curiosity perhaps, as they swim slowly past the diver's camera or the "window" of his helmet, yet none of the creatures exhibit the kind of wild panic that our human populations might fall into if strange monsters larger than ourselves (or in any case shaped very differently from ourselves) suddenly descended to our world through the atmospheric "ocean" which enfolds us.

Many centuries ago, sponges of the Mediterranean coastal waters were used to pad the helmets and shields of Greek warriors. At Ermioni, a town of the Argolide, and at other places, diving sports were held. All swimmers of those days were divers, and nearly every diver was a sponge fisherman. Sponges were used for many purposes by the Greeks, and although many sponges were washed ashore, the fishermen, centuries before Christ, had learned to go down into the sea and pluck them from the reefs. They went into the water naked, taking nothing with them except marble weights: the diver carried one in his left hand to carry him down to the sea bottom.

Heavy stones were undoubtedly the first devices used by men in penetrating the coastal waters to collect crustaceans, sponges and so on—they could be instantly released, enabling the divers to surface again—but such

138

diving, with or without stones, cannot be called "sea exploration". To early man the sea was a monster, inspiring fear rather than curiosity, and he had to develop confidence in himself by exploring his land surfaces before he ventured far across the oceans, or down to any considerable depth in the coastal waters.

Although the Greeks were the first to realize the value of the sponge as an article of commerce and develop it into a large industry, employing thousands of people and sometimes entire towns, the fact that it is of use to man in an infinite variety of ways suggests that it must have been known to primitive peoples, and that it must have been one of man's first incentives to explore the sea. The sponge thrives amongst marine grass and on flat sea-beds and is often thrown up on the shore, where, by the action of the waves, it is rolled in the sand and freed from its outer skin and sarcode, so that it was literally a gift to primitive man, inviting him to venture into the waters and find more.

The Egyptians and Phoenicians are believed to have discovered this natural throwing-up and cleansing process of the sponge, and it is probable that the latter introduced it to the Greeks, who began the sponge industry. Then for centuries the Dodecanese became the centres of sponge fishing—islands which included Kos, where Hippocrates, the father of medicine, lived; and Patmos, where John, the exiled mystic, wrote the *Revelation* of the Bible.

Sponge fishing spread to other parts of the world—to the Gulf of Mexico, where millions of sponges had multiplied in the warm waters, unmolested and commercially unexploited. Key West was the centre of the sponge industry there, but it was not until John K. Cheyney organized it in 1890, and began to buy and send out hooker boats from Tarpon Springs that the Gulf challenged the Dodecanese Islands as a sponge market. Divers came to Key West from the islands, and from Greece, bringing diving-suits and plans for diving boats, and also their families and family customs, their dress, language and dances, and their passionate love of colour and music, and of the sea itself. More than three thousand Greeks are now living in Key West, gathering great crops of sponges from the nine thousand square miles over which the industry now extends, and using boats which are little changed in shape—but equipped with Diesel engines—from those employed in sponge fishing for centuries in the Mediterranean.

Aristotle mentions the sponge as a "zoophyte"—an animal-plant akin to corals and sea-anemones—but it is now known to form a very distinct phylum or sub-kingdom, the *Porifera*, because of the water-pores with which it is provided in abundance.

All the sponges are aquatic, and most of them thrive in the sea. They vary widely in size from tiny sponges scarcely visible to the naked eye to great compound masses several feet in circumference. They also differ considerably in shape, because of their power of budding. They are many-celled, but the individuals in a colony (like the man-of-war, each sponge is a community) retain a considerable independence in their duties.

It is important to distinguish sponges from the Coelenterates—comprising jelly-fish, sea-anemones, corals, etc. The Coelenterates consist essentially of two main cell layers, although these may be elaborately folded, and the nervous system of one is always a net—never a central nervous system. The nerve net, however, may be especially well-developed around the mouth.

The sponge has no nervous system. Some authorities believe it has evolved from the Protozoa, along a separate line of descent from that of the other Metazoa (many-celled animals) but there is no evidence of any change in the sponge throughout its known history. It has always been as distinct, so far as human knowledge goes, as it is today.

But although the sponges must be sharply distin-

guished from the Coelenterates, they have many superficial resemblances to corals, and often share the same
habitats. Sponges are found in great abundance along
coral reefs in tropical waters, in fact such reefs have
corals for their main structure and sponges are one of the
most outstanding features. Sponges and their extraordinary natural behaviour will therefore be better understood if an account of them is preceded by an examination
of corals.

The sponges we handle in our bathrooms are skeletons.
The world's coral reefs consist of skeletons of countless
millions of polyps, so that sponges and corals have that
in common—they are skeletons of living creatures. In the
vertebrates (including man himself) the skeleton form is
based upon a backbone. Corals have "all over" skeletons : the creatures live inside structures which branch in
various directions. Crustaceans like crabs wear their
skeletons outside like armour. Sponges are interpene-
trated by their skeletons. When they die the hard
structure remains : in the corals such skeletons build up
the reefs; but in the sponges the structure (although
tougher and firmer than the gelatinous ground-sub-
stance) can be softened considerably so that the substance
is kind to our skins.

True corals may be roughly divided into two kinds.
There is the simpler, more primitive type of coral, forming a single calicle or coralite, as in the early Palaeozoic
cup-corals and certain existing species which live buried
in mud or extend in deep cold water over the sea-bed,
never rising to the surface. These corals are found in all
seas, from Greenland to the tropics.

The reef-building corals are more complex, and occur
in encrusting masses. But both types are polyps with
skeletons which interpenetrate them, strengthening their
bodies while they are alive, having fulfilled their rein-
forcement functions, remaining in the sea after the polyps
have died.

The coral polyp's building patterns are manifold. About 2,500 living, and 5,000 fossil, species are known. It secretes lime under its base, around its sides, and in radial ridges. Living polyps can withdraw themselves almost completely into the connected chambers formed by these ridges. It might be said of the creature, when it is inside, that it is living in all the rooms of its house at once. The shapes of the structures give the polyps their various names, and are self-explanatory: star coral, rose coral, organ-pipe coral, mushroom coral, and brain coral are some of them.

In most corals the sexes are separate, and even the reef growths may have areas entirely male or female. Hermaphrodites may occur, and there are even corals which have male and female branches in the individual. Semper says that there is at least one species in which the sex changes from male to female in alternate generations.

The richest and most impressive areas of the world's seas are the coral reefs, and of these the chain of shoals, shelves and islands along Australia's north-east coast, which forms the world's greatest coral structure and is known as the Great Barrier Reef, is our planet's finest "show-case" of the wonders of the sea.

Captain James Cook, whose ship was beached and damaged on a submerged reef one night in June 1770, at a place now known as Cooktown, was too anxious to repair his ship and sail on to Batavia, to appreciate the beauties of the island shores.

Even today the vast labyrinth of coral formations remains almost entirely undisturbed by man's explorations. Over five hundred of the Great Barrier Reef's sand-banks and islands remain unpeopled, while hundreds of thousands of coral grottoes have never been approached by divers. Because the visible surfaces of the mighty Reef are generally flat, they never drain dry between tides. Under skies of brilliant blue, untold multitudes of tiny sea animals are still building the Reef upwards, generation after generation leaving their limy skeletons behind as they die, to add their extremely thin layers to the deposits of countless ages. These are the years (a microscopic period of time in the eons during which generations of these amazing organisms have lived and died to produce the Reef) which mark the emergence of the vast structure from the sea. In other parts of the world many other coral reefs have already emerged or are slowly coming to the surface.

Coral reefs can be built only when the animals are washed by waters warm enough to assist the secretion of the calcareous substance which forms their skeletons. The living reef-structures, with all their associated life forms, must therefore be confined to waters with temperatures which do not fall below seventy degrees for more than very brief periods. They therefore occur only in the area bounded by the Tropics of Cancer and Capricorn, and mainly on the eastern shores of continents, bathed by currents of warm water carried towards the poles by the world's wind and tide patterns, under the influence of the earth's rotation.

Taking North America as an instance of this principle: the Pacific coast lacks corals, because they are affected by uprisings of cold water, while the north-eastern shores of Australia, washed by warmer currents, are the site of the Great Barrier Reef. The only coral coast within the United States is the two hundred-mile group of islands (actually two groups) known as the Florida Keys—second only to the Australian Reef itself for strange and beautiful corals in vast profusion.

Although coral *reefs*, consisting of the more massive kinds of coral, are confined to the sea's warmer waters, the more primitive kinds, already mentioned, are very widely distributed and are found at all depths, both in warm and cold waters. Certain varieties form dense beds off the coasts of Scotland, Norway and Portugal—but it must be reported that these are not the reef-building types.

There are three classes of coral reefs. Fringing reefs are platforms which extend to no great distance from the shores of a continent or island. Barrier reefs are fringing reefs on a large scale, with their outer edges much farther from the shores, and with deeper water separating them from the land. Atolls are ring-shaped reefs, either awash at low tide or crowned by several islets—sometimes by a strip of dry land ringing a central lagoon.

It was at one time supposed that coral was a calcified portion of the soft parts of the polyps. But this was disproved by Bourne and others, and it is now known that it is the solid support or skeleton, already described. The calcareous septa (or partitions) are deposited by the embryo polyp before it becomes firmly fixed to the sea bottom, or to other polyps' skeletons beneath itself. In the very young polyp of the Mediterranean *Astroides*, twelve calcareous partitions are deposited, and these, becoming fixed, are joined to the external walls (theca) of the coral, forming a groundwork or pedestal, a kind of limestone foundation on which the young polyp rests. Upon this the lime-structure grows as the polyps die and leave their skeletons behind them as part of the multiple structure which slowly builds up—in some cases spreading over the sea-bed and never approaching the surface, while in the case of the reef-building polyps rising, layer by layer, towards the surface of the sea through untold centuries.

Little is known, even today, regarding the rapidity of growth in corals. A specimen of *Meandrina labyrinthica* was taken from a block of concrete at Fort Jefferson, Tortugas, some time ago, which had been in the water only twenty years. It measured a foot in diameter and four inches in thickness. Another outstanding case of coral growth was examined on the wreck of a ship by the naturalist Verrill, who found that it had grown to a height of sixteen feet in sixty-four years—showing the extraordinary rate of three inches a year. But most authorities give the average rate of coral growth as about half this: one and a half inches a year, upward, over comparatively small areas, and a very much slower rate *when the polyps spread out.* Many centuries have elapsed in the building of the great reefs from the sea-bed.

Corals are free-swimming creatures only as embryos, and then for brief periods. They quickly imprison themselves in their limestone structures, secreted usually on their ancestors' skeletons. As time passes the individual structures are firmly cemented into masses, and these are even more firmly bound together by certain coralline algae. In the daytime, those living corals which are on the surface shrink into their stone fortresses. When darkness falls they extend tentacles to catch and poison planktonic creatures, which are carried to their mouths.

In every pool over the thousands of square miles of the Great Barrier Reef a kaleidoscopic variety of sea life swarms—gaudy coral fishes, tube worms gently waving their plumed gills, sea-stars, spiny urchins and countless other animals.

Clams of the genus *Tridacna* up to three feet long occur over the entire Reef. Although clams are eyeless they have organs which are sensitive to light, so that they can detect a man's moving shadow. When they sense that humans are passing near them in this way they close their shells quickly—the action in some cases being so violent that a stream of water may be shot several feet into the air. When they feel that danger is past they open again, and their gorgeous mantles emerge over the edges of their valves. Clams along the Great Barrier Reef are of many colours and sizes. Some of them have mantles of brilliant green, which, as they emerge from the valves, look like squirming snakes. Starfishes abound on the Reef —moving with hundreds of suckered feet, which are fixed in grooves running along each arm. Together with sea-urchins and other relatives they are known as echinoderms, meaning spiny skin.

Other life on and in the Reef are: hermit-crabs, which borrow the shells of other creatures for their houses; sea-wasps (a venomous kind of jelly-fish, the sting of which can be fatal to humans); cowries, with their brilliantly coloured mantles; and all kinds of crustaceans. Sting-rays lurk in the shallows, as obscure, ominous patches. Wedge-tailed shearwaters, called muttonbirds locally, burrow and build their nests underground—to mention only one of the extraordinary birds which fly in myriads over the Reef. Enormous crowds of soldier crabs—as large as a shilling—may suddenly invade a particular beach: only to vanish, if frightened, as suddenly as they appeared.

The warm waters of the world's coral reefs encourage the prolific breeding of all kinds of creatures, and numbers of these—like the giant *Crocodilus porosus*—reach dimensions far exceeding those of their normal relatives in colder waters. There are, for instance, the moray eels, which lurk in the coral crevices of many reefs, resenting the intrusions of divers and often snapping at them with their slit-like mouths, which are armed with long needle-sharp teeth. These have small heads and bead-like eyes, and are sometimes six feet in length. Clams weighing up to fifteen ounces are considered large specimens among the long (or soft-shelled) varieties, and the gaper (*Mya arenaria*) is among the moderately large British bivalves, although it is usually no more than four inches long and two and a half inches broad.* But the clams of the coral reefs are commonly ten, twenty or even a hundred times larger, while one species, *Tridacna gigantea*, may weigh as much as several men. One specimen, taken in Australia and now exhibited at the American Museum of Natural

*The largest British bivalve is the fan-shell, *Pinna fragilis*; specimens up to fifteen inches long and eight inches wide have been found.

History, weighs no less than 579½ pounds—over a quarter of a ton.

These are but few of the fantastic creatures which inhabit the coral reefs, and are the companions of the sponges.

For a long time sponges were thought to be plants, but we now know them as skeletons—each one the framework of a slime-animal. The sponge you hold in your hand may have come from the warm deep waters of the Grecian Archipelago, or it may have grown to maturity in the Red Sea. But the waters of the Mediterranean, the Dodecanese Islands, and the Gulf of Mexico, are the ideal environment for sponges—owing to their freedom from strong currents, and the favourable temperatures. Sponges are so prolific and of such fine quality in the Gulf of Mexico that it is now the world's largest sponge market.

Sponges are woven of a material that resembles the material spun by silk worms. When alive, the cells on the outside of the skeleton procure food and oxygen for the organism. They do this by using flagella—fine hair-like appendages—which whip the water into the canals, driving streams of it through them, so that the food and oxygen can penetrate through the whole system. Thomas Huxley described the sponge as a kind of submarine Venice, "where the people are ranged about the streets and roads in such a manner that each can easily appropriate its food from the water as it passes along".

As it grows at the bottom of the sea, on the ocean shelves, the living sponge is covered inside and out by a gelatinous substance which absorbs particles of floating matter as they pass through the canals. Those particles which are not nutritive are eventually rejected, passing out into the sea again. The creatures may be perpetuated by gemmation—the formation of new individuals by the protrusion and breaking away of parts of the parent. The little gemmule, or "bud", is carried out by the emerging water and swirled about until it at last fastens itself to a piece of rock or weed. This is but one of the sponge's methods of reproduction: by the breaking away of complex buds, asexually, each one protected by a spicule-sheath and capable of developing into a complete structure.

But most sponges reproduce sexually by the union of spermatozoön and ovum, resulting in the development of a free-swimming larva (planula)—this method serving not only to reproduce the species but to distribute it.

The pores, with which the surfaces of the sponge is furnished in abundance, are ordinarily of two kinds—the large ones (oscula) which are few in number, and are often guarded by special protective devices, such as circles of spicules or muscles capable of contracting the orifice; and the far more numerous inhalant pores everywhere perforating the wall-surfaces of the canals. The complicated "mechanism" of the sponge is still a mystery —how it is able to select nutritive substances and reject others; how it is able to create and cast off its gemmules; how it digests its food; how it controls its continually-waving flagella, so vital to the circulation of water through its canals: everything about the sponge is a baffling problem, challenging man's investigation.

In the higher flint-building sponges the structure is exquisite, for the spicules become complicated in the extreme and are bound together with fine, transparent flint threads which create a pattern resembling that of a valuable piece of lace. The sponge known as Venus's-basket is an example of this fine weaving. It seems incredible that it has not been woven by an artist in lace-making. It has all the beauty and transparency of finely-spun glass, or crochet-work created after years of patient labour by an expert in such a handicraft.

Like the Portuguese man-of-war, the sponge is a community structure, in which each tiny individual does its duty. Yet the flagella, as they whip the water and entice it into the canals, are apparently no more than simple appendages of the sponge itself, controlled by the sponge as our arms and legs are controlled by us. But they are really semi-independent individuals, and if we term them "devices", for want of a better name, we must be prepared to regard them as living, self-acting ones. They also occur in the *Flagellata*, motile unicellular organisms present in numerous plants and bacteria; in the spermatozoa (minute active gametes in the semen of multicellular creatures which serve to fertilize the ovum); and, as cilia, covering the respiratory, excretory, and reproductive systems of numerous animals, including ourselves.

Although some zoologists distinguish between flagella, which occur singly or in very small numbers as "whips" on unicellular creatures, and cilia, which occur in large numbers, the distinction cannot be justified. For the cilia are never simple "hairs" like eyelashes (the name derives from the Latin *cilium*, eyelids or eyelashes) but in all respects—structure, size and activity—are similar to flagella: both cilia and flagella are "whip-like" and usually in incessant vibratile movement.

In all such organelles—perhaps the best name for them, for they are both organisms and small organs— energy is somehow used to produce motion, but biologists find it extremely difficult to explain the nature of the process. One of our best authorities on the subject says simply, "We do not know." Flagellated cells are found in all the main divisions of the plant and animal kingdoms, with a few exceptions, and these cells serve either of two purposes: to move the cells through the water, when they are free-swimming creatures, or to move water past the cells, when they are the organs of larger organisms, like the sponge.

Protozoa of all kinds live as parasites in the sense that, even if they are not attached to larger creatures or (as cilia, which have all the characteristics of protozoa) ful-filling various purposes as parts of organs belonging to them, they live at the expense of other living animals.

As an instance of this "independent parasitism" we have the free-swimming flagellates of the sea.

Chief among ocean plants are the diatoms, which comprise more than half the oceanic plants, and are microscopic plants of the group *Diatomacea*, with cells composed of two symmetrical valves. They multiply by spontaneous separation. There are more than four thousand species of these tiny plants, scattered over the waters of the world, and their structures show an infinite variety of designs of great beauty, rivalling the diversity and perfection of snow crystals. Besides the diatoms there are certain species of blue-green algae and the flagellates, which compensate to some extent for their dependent and independent parasitism by manufacturing vegetable food in the sea. But when they exhibit malevolent qualities they can foul the waters so badly that they poison large numbers of fish.

They caused what was termed the "Red Tide" that washed the shores of Florida in 1947 and killed—it was estimated—over fifty million fishes, large numbers of which were washed up on the shores in such states of decomposition that they stank disgustingly. So thickly did they swarm in the sea on that occasion that a single pint of sea water was found to contain over sixty million flagellates.

The free-swimming flagellates of the ocean, therefore, present us with the paradox, that they can be enormously beneficial to ocean life, as creatures which are half plant, half animal, manufacturing protoplasm as the life-giving substance upon which myriads of fishes and other sea animals feed; and they can be life-destroyers when, by an excess of breeding, they poison vast numbers of other creatures of the sea.

All those forms of Protozoa classed as flagellata—

having cell-bodies provided with whip-like tails—are extremely complicated in structure and exhibit a vast range of designs, often singularly beautiful. Every conceivable pattern appears among them—circular shapes, oval ones, elongated forms, and others—numbers of them having radial and other designs which rival those of stained-glass windows.

Methods of feeding are variable. Food may be taken in at well-defined spots, sometimes but not necessarily oral, or it may be absorbed in solution through the general surface of the body.

The body structure is apparently simple in most cases, but this only makes the movements of the flagella more mysterious. Among the free-swimming flagellates we have enormous swarms of living creatures which, like the thread-slime, have no brains or nervous systems, yet control their activities as though they possessed either or both; have no stomachs, yet can digest their food; have no true eyes, yet can move about and direct themselves as though they can see; and have no sexual systems yet can reproduce themselves prolifically and perfectly.

Many spermatozoids and free-swimming algae cells have been observed moving at speeds which (considering their microscopic size) are comparatively far greater than any speeds attainable by humans using cars or aircraft. One species of the ciliated protozoa, using its flagella to attain the speed, has been scientifically timed at two thousand microns per second—nearly six inches a minute. Comparing the relative size of the creature with the distance, man would need to travel at thousands of miles a minute to attain comparable speeds.

Realizing that the flagella and the cilia are so similar in their structures and characteristics that it is impossible to classify them separately, the wide range of their activities can be generally listed. They run right through the plant kingdom from single-celled algae and mosses and ferns; through the animal kingdom from

Protozoa to invertebrates and upwards to such weird creatures as squids, and upwards again from them, through fishes of many kinds, to mammals like ourselves. Everywhere, through countless myriads of life-forms are these waving "hairs" which are organs which baffle the most detailed examination.

The cilia tracts—hairy surfaces—around the throats of such protozoic creatures as *Paramecium* and *Vorticella* are specialized filter-feeding mechanisms—so are the ciliated rings around the mouths of rotifers, which get their name from the curious "spinning" effect caused by the rapid movement of the whip-like hairs as they flash rapidly around each pulsating ring.

Oysters and mussels use these microscopic whips, for their gills are covered with a ciliated epithelium or outer layer, over which a constant stream of mucus flows, catching particles of food and conveying them to the creature's open gullet.

Few people realize, when they clear their throats of phlegm, that they are only able to do so (saving their lungs from accumulations of mucus) because their throats are lined with cilia similar to those which carry particles of food into the gullets of oysters. We call these microscopic "hairs" which line our throats cilia, but, like all cilia of the types we have been considering, our "throat-hairs" have all the characteristics of flagella. The oyster's "whips" wave the food particles into its gullet; the sponge's waving flagella beckon microscopic planktonic sea creatures into its canals; and the whips which line the throat of a man are continually in action passing particles of injurious dust upwards until they reach his nose and mouth, mixed with the mucus without which the flagella cannot act (for they always operate in liquids) and so being carried *out* of the human organism, even as food particles are carried *into* the organisms of sponges, molluscs and other creatures.

So in the process of conception, ciliated tracts, also

152

covered with mucus, possess flagella which "wave" the egg-cells onwards and downwards, so that they may be fertilized by the spermatozoa, which ascend towards them by using their own flagella—their whip-like tails. Neither the larger egg-cells of the female, nor the tadpole-like spermatozoa of the male, could manage their extraordinary journeys unaided, although the spermatozoa have a kind of semi-independent motion as they oscillate their flagella: they both need the propulsive help of the waving "whips" which line the female Fallopian tube.

Whether we consider them as devices, plants or animals—and all three terms are applicable—we are compelled to believe that flagellates are baffling and mysterious, in all their diversified forms, from those which create the light in the water (wrongly described as "phosphorescent") when disturbed in their myriads by the passing of a steamer, to those which may break away from a human throat, be ejected in mucus, and swim for some time (like living protozoa in the sea, with independent life and action) within that discharged mucus.

We have apparently travelled a long way from the sponge, but it is here a case of the longest way round being the shortest way home. For no appreciation of the real nature of a sponge's flagella would be possible without some idea of the enormous diversity of cilia and flagella in the animal and vegetable kingdoms.

Sponges in millions occur in the world's coral reefs. Others thrive in areas where there are no corals. Some sponges are non-aggressive: others are almost ferocious as they bore their way into solid rock. All sponges have their flagella, linking them with plants and animals and with man himself in curious relationships which indicate the underlying unity of all living creatures.

CHAPTER IX

THE FISHMEN

MAN'S first penetrations of the sea were confined to wadings, dives and underwater swimming in shallow waters. His first boats—hollowed-out tree trunks—were used on rivers, and countless centuries passed before any attempts were made to cross the world's seas, for they were regions which early man, in his imagination, peopled with dragons, centaurs, vengeful deities, and fabulous beasts of all kinds. The sea itself was often personified as a monster, vested with enormous powers of destruction, and subject to fits of anger and sullen treachery—a being to be propitiated and never offended by undue curiosity regarding its fearsome secrets.

Sponges were certainly among the very first creatures of the sea which attracted primitive man into the shore-waters, and they were probably among the first artificial aids used in his diving ventures. It may be difficult to realize that the sponge was one of the primitive, crude progenitors of the bathyscaphe, but such was undoubtedly the case.

A stone held in the hand was probably the very first "diving appliance"; one which was used by the divers of Greece countless centuries later (as noted in the last chapter) and is still used today by uncivilized peoples. But a sponge held in the mouth was also a very early device to assist submarine exploration.* It was a step

---

*Several old writers say that sponge-divers were able to use the air trapped in the sponge. A modern author suggests that the diver bit the sponge when under water, and that this released oil which calmed and cleared the water around him.

nearer the diving suit and the bathyscaphe, although a very elementary "invention", for (dipped in oil of some kind) it helped him to breathe under water. This practice continued through the centuries until quite recent times, particularly among sponge divers of the Mediterranean.

Dr. Halley, the noted astronomer and naturalist, writing while modern exploration of the sea was still in its infancy and before cumbersome diving suits and "diving bells" had reached any degree of perfection, said that "without a sponge, a naked diver cannot remain above two minutes enclosed in water; nor much longer with one, without suffocating". He added, "Nor without long practice near so long: ordinarily persons beginning to be suffocated in less than half a minute. Besides, if the depth be considerable, the pressure of the water in the vessels makes the eyes blood-shotten, and frequently occasions a spitting of blood." A contemporary of Dr. Halley, writing in confirmation of his statements, said: "It is found by experiment that a gallon of air included in a bladder, reciprocally inspired and expired by the lungs, becomes unfit for respiration in little more than a minute of time."

Dr. Halley achieved immortality by the brilliance and accuracy of his astronomical observations. His suggestions inspired Newton to write his *Principia*. He made the first complete observation of a transit of Mercury. He was Astronomer Royal towards the close of the eighteenth century. He accurately predicted the return of the comet which was named after him. But his knowledge of divers and diving was ludicrously inadequate.

Marine products used by ancient peoples provide abundant evidence that divers in many countries had become highly proficient in naked underwater exploration for many centuries before Halley used the words quoted. Red coral was regarded as a mystical substance and exported from the Mediterranean shores to places as far away as China, over two thousand years ago: quite recent history when related to the sea explorations of primitive man, but old enough, when considered with other historical facts, to set us wondering at the naïveté of Dr. Halley's statements.

The ancient Greeks used many products which could only have been obtained from the sea-beds of the coastal waters. A certain shellfish contributed a dye for the Imperial purple. Roman soldiers used sponges as canteens on their marches. A sponge soaked in vinegar was offered to Christ on the cross. Shells from the shores, numbers of which could only have been obtained by divers, were built into medieval cathedrals, particularly those of the great *Tridacna* clam, which were often used for fonts. Dr. Halley must surely have known some of these historical facts and of the exploits of pearl divers; and other naked underwater swimmers of his own times. Yet he specifically states the limit of underwater endurance "ordinarily" as half a minute, and of experienced divers as two minutes.

The main problem of naked diving without appliances was always that of holding the breath long enough to accomplish some task under water or on the sea-bed. Pearl divers, from earliest times, have always been able to stay under water for periods exceeding three minutes, and there are numerous well-authenticated instances of divers going down to a hundred feet or more, and remaining under for longer periods.

One of the most remarkable cases in recent times—on account of the depth attained, apart from the period of endurance—is that of a Greek sponge diver named Stotti Georghios. Wearing no breathing apparatus, fins or eyeglasses (and not even carrying a stone or a sponge) he went down to a depth of two hundred feet in 1913 to attach a line to the lost anchor of the Italian battleship *Regina Margharita*. At that depth the pressure on his lungs was enormous—they were squeezed by seven atmospheres of pressure, which should have been enough to collapse them to half their diameter. His breath control was little short of miraculous, not only in remaining under for over four minutes, but in resisting the pressure at that depth until he had accomplished his task.

The *Amas* of Japan, professional divers attached to the Mikimoto culture-pearl industry of today, make as many as eighty or ninety dives daily and (wearing nothing but their goggles) frequently go down to depths exceeding 120 feet, and remain under water without breathing apparatus for periods exceeding three and a half minutes. The world's record for remaining under water far exceeds four minutes. It was set at San Rafael, California, by Dr. Robert Keast, thirty-four years of age, on 18th March 1956. The previous world's record, which Dr. Keast tried to beat, was 6 minutes 29.8 seconds: made forty-four years earlier in 1912.

Dr. Keast shattered that record by remaining under, conserving his breath, for 10 minutes 58.9 seconds—only one and a tenth second under eleven minutes.

Depth pressure is not the handicap to diving that one might imagine. The human body has almost the same density as salt water itself, and the flesh of man resembles that of fish in its power of resisting compression. Only the hollow organs in man, such as his lungs, are in danger when subjected to pressure in the depths. Naked divers, by long practice and intensive training, can develop their lungs to resist enormous pressures for brief periods.

In his naked diving feats, without any kind of apparatus, man's nearest competitors have always been certain birds: among them a family of swimming birds popularly known as Divers, the *Colymbidae*. On land these birds are awkward creatures, shuffling along with their breasts to the ground, as though embarrassed and made awkward by contact with solid surfaces. They seldom take wing, and rise with difficulty, but when they are air-borne they sweep along very rapidly, especially when they migrate or change their abodes from the sea to inland lakes or vice versa.

The term "diver" is often applied, vaguely, to birds which have no right to the name, such as several of the sea ducks, some of the mergansers, and certain auks and grebes; but British ornithologists agree that the word should be restricted to the *Colymbidae*, a clearly defined group possessing considerable powers of submergence.

In common with the grebes—but thereby differing from other birds—the divers possess curious anatomical structures which help them to swim. The wings are small, concave and composed of stiff feathers, so that they can use them as oars when underwater and giving chase to submerged fishes, or escaping from their underwater enemies.

In the diver, the crest of the tibia is prolonged upwards to unite with the kneecap (patella), so that a spike-like projection is formed at the extremity of the bone, which gives the bird a considerable advantage in the act of swimming by reason of its efficient leverage. The limbs are placed as far back as possible, and the tarsus is flattened laterally to cleave the water. The toes, which are either lobated or webbed, are so formed that they close into a small compass when drawn towards the body in preparation for a stroke. The plumage is close, silky and very glossy. The tail is either short or wanting altogether. The body is flat, oval and "stream lined", and from its rather depressed contour appears to float more deeply in the water than it actually does.

The great northern diver (*Colymbus glacialis*) is the largest species of the genus, and may attain a length of as much as three feet. It is met chiefly in the Arctic regions, but comes farther south with the approach of winter. It is a beautiful bird, characterized by its glossy black head and neck and the presence of two gorgets (or semi-collars) of velvet-black and pure white vertical stripes on its throat, and belts of white spots contrasting sharply with its dark back, the under parts of the bird being white.

The commonest species is the red-throated diver (*C. septentrionalis*), which has an elongated colour patch on its throat as an adult, when in its summer dress, which gives the bird its name. It inhabits the north temperate zone of both hemispheres.

C. glacialis has been said to breed in Scotland and in Norway, but (with the exception of Iceland) it is doubtful if it is indigenous to the Old World.

Two remarkable occurrences in connection with the great northern diver may be of interest. According to J. Vaughan Thompson in his *Natural History of Ireland*, one of these divers was shot off the Irish coast some years ago, and was found to have "an arrow headed with copper sticking through its neck"; while another diver of the same species was found dead in Kalbaksfjord in The Faeroes with an iron-tipped bone dart fast under its wing. Considering that both birds had apparently crossed the Atlantic, and that darts or arrows in birds are not common occurrences, it is remarkable that these things should have happened to birds of this one species, out of the thousands of species of known birds.

The divers go under water without exertion, and, when swimming, their bodies are almost entirely immersed—only the head and neck appearing above the surface. After swimming for some time like this they will suddenly submerge completely and travel under water for considerable distances without coming up again. In contrast with their clumsiness on land they show great agility both on the surface and when submerged, and may be regarded as serious rivals to human divers in their feats of underwater endurance. There are well-authenticated cases of the great northern diver remaining completely under water for eight minutes and longer.

Frank Lane in his *Nature Parade* gives some remarkable

facts regarding swimming birds. He mentions the gannet as being one of the most efficient of all feathered divers. It sometimes makes a precipitous dive into the sea from a height of over one hundred feet, at an estimated speed of one hundred miles an hour. The force with which the bird strikes the water may be estimated from the fact that a diving gannet, coming in contact with a board sunk to a depth of six feet, has driven its beak so firmly into the wood that its neck has been broken.

Gannets have copious supplies of oil in their glands for water proofing their feathers. Bird plumage always offers some resistance to water, but the water proofing is more efficient in aquatic birds. Sooty terns, which sometimes rest on water, become waterlogged in a few hours if they remain on it, but ducks can sleep on the surface for a whole night.

Birds can control the resistance of their feathers to water, probably by manipulation of the muscles at the feather roots. Batten, in *Inland Birds* says that wild ducks may swim and dive with their under-feathers quite dry, but if one is shot and falls into the water the plumage is immediately saturated. Dr. Bastian Schmid has told an extraordinary story of some Indian runner ducks which he kept: the birds had never seen a pond, having been reared by a hen. Dr. Schmid sprinkled them lightly with a watering-can one day, and this caused them to go through all the motions of swimming and diving.

Some diving birds have been observed to leave the surface of the water flapping their wings, showing that they had been using them to "fly" to the surface, and had then continued to use them, without a pause, to ascend through the air.

Closely allied to diving birds are the penguins—which form the very distinct order *Impennes*, and family *Spheniscidae*. The penguin has many resemblances to the diver in the structure of its softer internal parts, and in the backward position of its short legs and upright posture when on land. The penguins of the southern hemisphere differ from all other members of their class in two important features: the wings, in which the quills are rudimentary, are transformed into paddles; and the short metatarsus (the group of five long bones of the foot lying between the tarsus and the toes) is of great width, with its three longitudinal elements fused together. The young are quite helpless when born and are tended with remarkable care by the mothers.

They exist in enormous numbers in the Antarctic seas and on the South African and American coasts, being found in large communities at Tierra del Fuego and on the Pacific Islands; also in Australia and New Zealand. They are gregarious creatures and have the habit of standing in long, regular lines, resembling files of soldiers on parade. The female Adélie incubates the eggs, which she protects by holding them between her thighs. She carries the eggs in the same peculiar fashion when disturbed or alarmed. The father penguin supplies both mother and baby with food during the period of incubation, and both parents feed the young when hatched.

The nests are formed in the hollows of rocks, and the eggs are deposited on the thick layer of excrement which —accumulating over long periods—constitutes some of the valuable guano of commerce.

Despite its waddling gait, which might suggest that it is a clumsy animal, the penguin is the most expert swimmer of all birds. Everything in its structure contributes to this: its "cutwater" beak; its close-fitting feathers, which might almost be called scales; its powerful flippers, which can move independently; its tail and legs which can act together both as rudder and brake; and its streamlined body.

Penguins can attain twelve miles an hour easily, and can reach eighteen when pursuing a fast fish. Murphy, in his *Oceanic Birds* gives the speed of the gentoo penguin when going "all out" as twenty-two miles an hour. That they possess unusual agility and strength is shown by the fact that they have been observed to shoot up out of the water and land on ledges of ice more than five feet high.

The penguins of Tristan da Cunha migrate about April and return in July or August, but where they go remains somewhat of a mystery—it seems incredible that they should remain at sea for such a protracted period.

The emperor penguin is truly a royal bird, for he normally stands three feet tall and weighs ninety pounds. But there are outsize ones. One captured by Captain Scott's men in 1911 was four feet tall and weighed seven stone. In the autumn this penguin heads south towards the pole and the coldest weather. The female hatches out the single egg after her arrival, and then father, mother and child head south again, into a less frigid climate. There is much commonsense in this hatching of the chick during the long Arctic night, for only in this way is it possible to rear the infant to the point where it is able to resist the rigours of the following winter.

The emperor penguin may be one of the most primitive birds. The growth of the embryo within the egg recapitulates the history of the species, and this history seems to suggest that the emperor has certain features in common with those of some reptiles.

Nearly every feature of a penguin caricatures something human: its black back and (usually) immaculate "white shirt front", which suggest man's evening dress; its sleek flippers which look like the arms of well-pressed but overlong sleeves: its drilling and marching habits, and the way penguins gather together in small groups, as if they were gossiping or discussing the political situation.

The penguin's resemblance to a human being is heightened by its "spectacles"—a white ring around each quizzical "black shoe-button" eye. Penguins walk quickly, despite their characteristic "waddling"—at the rate of about one hundred and twenty steps per minute.

Of the seventeen known species of the penguin indigenous to the southern hemisphere, only two are found in the Antarctic. The king penguin, not so large as the emperor, is found over a wider area. Closely allied to these is the smaller *Pygoscelis toeniata*, a gentle creature distinguished by its pointed red beak and with a stouter and more feathered body. It is commonly known as the "Johnny".

Still smaller and more numerous is the Adélie, which grows to about two feet tall and weighs only twelve pounds. This is the penguin with the best defined "spectacles". Of all the penguins the Adélies are the greatest travellers. In spring they journey five hundred miles back to their Antarctic homes, and have been observed nearly a thousand miles from them. Such distances are enormous for penguins to travel, most of the way on foot. But when penguins have long distances to go they conserve foot energy by turning themselves into sledges, especially down gradients. They flop on their stomachs and paddle themselves over the snow and ice by using their flippers like oars.

It is generally known that the male penguin makes gifts of pebbles to his lady, but less well known that he prefers to steal these from other birds' collections rather than search for pretty ones himself. Leaning forward, feathers drawn close, he tries to make himself inconspicuous and sneaks up to another penguin's wife as she broods on her nest and steals a stone from under her tail. If noticed by the husband before he gets to the nest he fluffs his feathers and strolls up and down with a nonchalant expression, looking very innocent.

As many as fifty thousand penguins have been counted in one area, crowded on pebble-cluttered nests, only a foot or so apart. Remarkable facts about the penguin are as prolific as the bird itself—it would require hundreds of pages of print to exhaust them—but mention must be made of the fact that, while some creatures (such as the bee and the ant) show uncanny skill in sex-determination, the penguin sometimes confuses the sexes of his own species. Male and female are indeed difficult to distinguish, but one would imagine that the penguin himself would possess discrimination. Yet he will sometimes take a pretty pebble to another male, mistaking him for an eligible young lady.

The jackass penguin is perhaps the most extraordinary of them all. Darwin says that when crawling on "all fours" on the shore it possesses an agility of motion in that attitude which is denied to all other penguins. It can *run* on all-fours, even along the slope of a grassy cliff, and at such a speed that it might well be mistaken for a quadruped. This species derives its popular name from its habit of throwing back its head and braying like a donkey.

Man's nearest competitors in underwater exploration, the divers and penguins, can put up good performances against his efforts as long as man uses no appliances. But man is a tool-using animal, a fact that distinguishes him from all others, and he has left his diving rivals far behind by his invention of appliances during the centuries, particularly in the more recent developments of undersea exploration.

The Portuguese man-of-war and a few other creatures have used their dependent tentacles or streamers as "sounding lines" for untold ages, but there has been no development in them—they are appliances which can only be used to "sound" any shallow shore areas in which such creatures find themselves. The man-of-war's tentacles cannot reach down beneath the surface beyond a hundred feet at the extreme limit.

Man's use of the sounding line—the third of his most primitive devices for sea exploration: the other two being the stone (held in his hands and later tied to his feet) and the sponge—was very probably an extension of its use for fishing.

The history of soundings is lost in antiquity, even as the

earlier records of sea explorations of all kinds are lost. We surmise that man's knowledge of the sea was limited to depths of about two hundred fathoms until recent times, but we know practically nothing of man's adventures or inventions in the long centuries before the Christian era.

The destruction of the Alexandrian libraries (begun by a mob of fanatical pseudo-Christians in A.D. 391, and completed at the taking of Alexandria by the Arabs two hundred and fifty years later) deprived mankind of an enormous amount of recorded knowledge of earlier sea exploration: with it, no doubt, numerous accounts of attempts to penetrate the sea's surface, by the use of sounding devices, and underwater appliances of all kinds. Four hundred and ninety thousand volumes or rolls (some authorities estimate that the collection contained nearly 700,000, with some duplicates) were lost forever.

There are many museums and other institutions which contain specimens of old-time sounding, dredging and diving devices, notably a fine one at Monaco, but explanations of their use in the form of accounts or records are rare and unreliable before the burning of the Alexandrian library. Herodotus mentions ocean soundings, and there are such references to them as those which occur in the account of St. Paul's shipwreck, in the Acts of the Apostles (where they took soundings and "found it twenty fathoms") but as we recede in history we realize that there must have been numerous soundings, divings and explorations (of which we have only isolated accounts) for thousands of years after primitive man had overcome his fear of the sea.

Mother-of-pearl, which cannot be picked up in any quantities on the shore, and must be sought for by diving, has been found in excavated ornaments of the Sixth Dynasty Thebes—about 3,200 B.C., and even in earlier excavations, in smaller amounts, going back a thousand years. But such finds tell us little of the explorations of the sea which produced them.

There are innumerable legends regarding early sea exploration: stories of underwater caves, and treasures brought out of the sea, and of devices used in exploring the sea. We have, for instance, the legend (one of many) regarding Alexander the Great (356–323 B.C.), found in the old script known as the *Pseudo-Kallisthenes*, in which it is stated that Alexander descended into the ocean depths with two companions in a vessel made from some transparent material and the skins of asses, and that they remained deep under water for ninety-six days and nights, observing the wonders of the ocean, seeing, among other strange creatures, a monstrous fish, of such length that it took four days to swim past their hiding place. As an account of early sea exploration the legend —like many others of the kind—is worthless; but it has some value in its implication that men were probably concerned with penetrating the sea's surface, even in those days. For the phrase "skins of asses", used to describe some of the material of the fabulous "diving bell" seems to be satirical and indicative of the existence of real devices, however ineffective.

The history of underwater exploration can be sharply divided into three sections: Accounts of divers who have gone down, either naked or with appliances, simple and complex, to help them descend and ascend, and to help them to breathe: humans who may have been encased in suits, but who have not used "diving bells" or similar vessels for their explorations—and accounts of humans who have gone down in contrivances which they have occupied, as pilots or "passengers". Divers in the first classification range from naked divers with no appliances whatever, to our modern frogmen and divers who use the aqualung or any similar device to assist breathing; and of course men wearing the older types of diving-suit with tubes connecting them with surface pumps are included. For convenience we term all these "fishmen". Those in the other classification, who occupy vessels within which they have freedom of movement—such as diving bells and bathyscaphes—will be considered in a later chapter, for these divers go down to far greater depths. The fishmen—both skin-divers and those who use diving-suits—are compelled to operate in shallower waters, for their bodies could not withstand the tremendous pressures of the greater depths.

Man must have air to breathe, but if that was his sole requirement in going down into the sea, and his body could stand the increasing pressures, it might be possible to send divers down (with tubes connecting them to the surface) to far greater depths than those which are now traversed by men in diving-suits. But the crushing pressure of the waters—increasing by nearly half a pound (actually 0.445 pounds) per square inch for every foot of depth—operates like a stern command: "Thus far shalt thou go and no farther." The deeper chasms of the oceans go down for miles, but the diver who is not protected from pressure by a shell of some kind—of steel several inches thick if he wants to descend thousands of feet—must confine his activities to the shore-waters of the continental shelves.

Perhaps the earliest reliable reference to unassisted or natural diving occurs in the *Iliad*, where Patroclus compares the fall of Hector's charioteer with the action of a diver diving for oysters.

Thucydides was the first to mention the employment of divers for mechanical work under water. He describes how divers were employed during the siege of Syracuse to saw through the barriers which had been constructed under the surface to obstruct and damage any Grecian vessels which might attempt to enter the harbour. There can be no doubt that divers, even in those early times, had so trained themselves that their lungs could resist the increasing pressures—doubled at thirty-three feet down, tripled at sixty-six feet, quadrupled at ninety-nine feet, and so on. We must accept the evidence of modern times, that naked divers can descend without apparatus to over a hundred feet, steeling themselves against the tremendous pressure at such depths.

Men had no knowledge of the real depths of the ocean until quite recently. Not until 1504 were soundings—made in shallow waters—first shown on a map: one drawn by Juan de la Costa. Deeper soundings were shown on Mercator's maps in 1585; after which it became the practice, increasingly, to incorporate them in most maps. Captain Cook, in his voyagings round the world, was the first to employ them systematically—using pieces of lead or cannon-balls. Captain Ross followed his example by using them in his Antarctic explorations.

The last use of hempen cord for soundings on an extensive scale was on the famous *Challenger* voyage of 1872–76. This Admiralty ship, in her explorations of the under waters in many parts of the world, often trailed her sounding line—sometimes as much as eight miles of it dragging behind her.

Lord Kelvin, the noted British mathematician and physicist devised the modern sounding apparatus in 1872, using piano-wire, which superseded the use of rope and enabled mankind to plumb greater depths more efficiently. Less than one-twentieth of an inch in diameter, the wire has tremendous tensile strength, more than ten times that of the finest hemp.

Sounding lines are supplementary aids to both classes of divers—fishmen and "sphere passengers". They have two purposes. They register depths and they also disclose the type of life below, and the nature of sediments, etc., samples of which they can bring to the surface for inspection and analysis. That is why fathometers (echo sounding devices) can never entirely replace the use of the line.

Countless centuries elapsed between primitive man's use of his fishing line to measure the depth of the shore waters and Kelvin's piano-wire. Those early men had lines made from creepers or grasses, only a few score fathoms in length, which they lowered slowly into the water and withdrew as carefully again. Kelvin's invention enabled navigators to unreel six hundred feet of wire in a minute, and to rewind it almost as rapidly.

The devices used by fishmen in these modern times are innumerable. Goggles were among the earliest modern inventions. They were quickly followed by extensions of them into masks of all kinds, one of the latest in use being the full-face type, with a snorkel built into it : a breathing device consisting of a tube, generally plastic, leading from the mask to a position above the head. With all the smaller goggles and masks (without compressed air supply or oxygen) the wearer has to hold his breath every time he looks down into the water. Using the snorkel mask there is no feeling of air-starvation—the breath is held only when preparing to dive. A valve attachment closes the tube immediately on diving and opens it again on returning to the surface.

All kinds of fins have been invented—some with closed heels, for instance, for protection against sharp coral. Swimmers can travel faster with "web-feet" fins, without using their arms, than if they were using all four limbs *without* fins.

There are also many types of under-water gun. The original "spear-gun" used in the Pacific was a simple contrivance—just a piece of steel tube or bamboo about a foot long, with a set of rubber bands attached to one end, often taken from an old inner tube. The "spear" might be any piece of metal with a barb on one end— perhaps an old bicycle spoke. The gun was "loaded" by passing the "spear" into it. All that was needed to fire it was to pull back the elastic, holding the end of the "spear" in it, and then—let fly.

There are all kinds of spear-guns, some spring-powered developments of the elastic-band type, and more powerful ones using cartridges. Some of these fire fifty or sixty shots from a magazine.

Spear-points may be explosive. One type, the Bel-Aqua Thunderhead is an impact powder-head which enables the user to kill big fish. There are also many kinds of knives, and a variety of gloves. Many diving spearmen wear only one glove—on the hand not used for firing the gun. Some gloves are not merely protective but webbed, serving a double purpose: enabling the wearer to hold on to coral, or grab a poisonous fish, and also giving him a little extra speed through the water.

Special waterproof flashlights are used for night diving. There are underwater compasses specially made for divers, with luminous dials; spectacle frames for divers with poor sight, which fit inside the masks; waterproof watches; and even underwater scooters! These are strapped to the body and have paddles operated by the feet. They are said to increase the diver's underwater speed by as much as three hundred per cent.

Underwater cameras have reached a high degree of perfection. There are now, in many countries, some thousands of underwater photographers, from amateurs using Brownies in football-bladders to professional movie cameramen using hundreds of miles of film a year as they record the habits of sea creatures and the adventures of the divers who are investigating them.

Weighted belts are sometimes used to facilitate faster and deeper descents, even by divers operating without self-contained oxygen appliances. These are so devised that they can be released instantly in emergencies. Fathometers are now available in many sporting goods stores. The appliance is strapped to the knee, and registers the depth of the diver. For those on the surface, watching the diver as he goes down, there are many new inventions, including waterscopes (developed from the old-fashioned glass-bottomed boxes used by the natives) which contribute to the high efficiency of modern sea exploration.

Underwater photography has become a specialized science. Cameras are dangled on cables, towed on sleds and taken down to the depths in bathyscaphes. Some of these, and the latest deep-sea underwater lamps, will be described in a later chapter.

Many pioneers in underwater exploration have been credited with the invention of the first self-contained breathing apparatus, including Giovanni Borelli in the seventeenth century and several inventors in recent decades. Lieutenant Philippe Taillez, who has many brilliant inventions to his credit in connection with sea exploration and who forms a distinguished trio of sub-marine explorers with Cousteau and Dumas, was one of the first of the mask divers to devise an efficient breathing tube. He made it from a heavy garden hose, and it had the decided advantage that it could be struck while under water without damaging it or imperilling the life of the diver—it was resilient and therefore simply regained its upright position. Some of the hook shapes are easily fouled by underwater obstacles. The basic principle of the Taillez invention has not been superseded by a more efficient one.

But even Borelli, over two and a half centuries before Taillez, was not the originator of the self-contained breathing apparatus. The first historical mention of any such invention is by Aristotle (384–322 B.C.). In his *De Partibus Animalium* he states that divers of his time were provided with instruments of respiration through which they could draw air from above the water, to enable them to remain for some time under the sea. In another work (*Problem* 32, 5) he says that divers were able to breathe by letting down a vessel which did not get filled with water, but retained the air within it. Pliny (A.D. 23–79) wrote of divers engaged in warfare, who used tubes through which they drew in air and expelled it—the upper end of the tube floating on the surface. Aristotle's words have often been quoted, and no doubt contain the earliest detailed descriptions of breathing mechanisms. But there were earlier pictorial representations. The London British Museum contains what may well be the earliest: two Assyrian bas-reliefs, dated about 900 B.C., which came from the palace of King Assur-Nasir-Pal at Nineveh. These show a number of men wearing inflated goatskins at their girdles. Each diver has a short tube in his mouth, connecting with a goatskin, through which he breathes air. Although some archaeologists have suggested that the appliance depicted was used to support soldiers swimming across rivers, the explanation does not account for the tubes, which would have had no purpose if the bags were merely early "water-wings"; in fact if the breathing apparatus idea is dismissed one might as well believe that the soldiers are playing bagpipes.

Roger Bacon is credited with the invention of an underwater breathing device in 1240.

Giovanni Alfonso Borelli (1608–79) was the first to introduce an efficient means of forcing air down to the diver. Modern authors have various misdescriptions of his apparatus. One says the gear was never tested and that the helmet was of brass or tin. But descriptions of Borelli's diving-suit, much nearer to his own time—some of them exhibiting considerable detail—show that it was far superior to the diving bells then being developed. One account says that it was devised for diving under the water to "great depths"—but the phrase did not in those days imply what it does today. The vesica or bladder (actually the headpiece) was of brass or copper—certainly not tin—and was about two feet in diameter. It was fixed to a goatskin suit, "exactly fitting the body of the person". Within the headpiece were pipes by which a circulation of air was contrived.

The diver was connected with a bellows on the surface,

so that he was independent of helpers above him. He carried "an air-pump at his side", and by manipulating this he could not merely supply himself with air but "make himself heavier or lighter, as do fishes by contracting or dilating their airbladders".

One account says that "the objections of all other diving-machines are obviated, particularly those regarding the air, the moisture of which is clogged in respiration, and by which it is rendered unfit for use again, being taken from it by its circulation through the pipes, to the sides of which it adheres, leaving the air as free as before". Other accounts say that the diver inhaled through his nose and exhaled through his mouth into a short pipe which led into a leathern bag. Borelli was certainly the pioneer of our age in self-contained breathing mechanisms, with all respect to pioneers of past ages.

Even if (as some assert) Borelli's apparatus was never adequately tested, it certainly contributed a great deal to the perfection of the diving-suit. Numbers of other inventors in various countries began experimenting with underwater apparatus as a result of his labours. One of these, a Devonshire man named John Lethbridge, seems to have had unusual success, contemporaneously with Borelli.

Lethbridge's suit was of strong leather, and various accounts agree that it contained "a hogshead of air", and was so contrived that none of it could escape. Glass was used for the front of the helmet. It was said that when he had put on the suit he could not only walk along the sea-bed near the shore, completely submerged, but could also enter the cabins of sunken ships, "to convey goods out of them at his pleasure". Lethbridge is credited with carrying on all kinds of salvage operations over a period of more than forty years, and with having made a considerable fortune from the use of his invention.

Borelli's ideas were materially advanced by Fréminet, a Frenchman, in 1772; and there can be no doubt that

173

his dives were successful. He used a leather suit with a copper helmet, and the air supply—from a small reservoir connected to the helmet—was water-cooled and circulated back to the diver. With this apparatus divers were able to stay under water for short periods, but if we dismiss accounts of Borelli's and Lethbridge's inventions as inadequately substantiated (and some of the accounts credit Borelli with the perfection of a boat that could be rowed under water!) the diving-suit was still not perfected.

Kleingert of Breslau, in 1798, incorporated much of the experience of his predecessors in the completion of what might well be regarded as the first practical and self-contained breathing mechanism. The diver was weighted for his descent, and released his weights when he wanted to rise, being hauled to the surface as he held on to a rope. Two pipes from above the surface gave him fresh air and carried away the foul air from his lungs. His apparatus was repeatedly used for depths up to twenty feet.

William H. James is sometimes credited with having invented the first self-contained diving-suit supplied with compressed air, in 1825. But Augustus Siebe, introducing his first diving-suit six years earlier, forestalled him, and James's invention was never tested. Siebe's first diving-suit was the "open" one in which the air escaped from under the diver's tunic around his waist, but he modified his original suit in 1837, by making it the now familiar "closed" dress of deep-sea divers, with air pumped under pressure from the surface. In 1878, H. A. Fleuss, in association with Siebe, Gorman and Company, brought the diving-suit to a state of perfection that has ensured its use ever since.

As first introduced it provided a continuous supply of oxygen from the helmet, where it was stored in a compressed state, the supply being regulated by the diver. The carbonic acid exhaled was absorbed by caustic soda.

The diver required only one attendant. He was enabled to move freely among wreckage, and he could signal to the surface efficiently. The suit became the standard equipment for all kinds of underwater operations, and was given rigorous tests—at the flooding of the Severn Tunnel, for instance, and on various occasions when mines were flooded, as at the Killingworth Colliery in 1882.

Many improvements have been effected in diving-suits since. A modification of the closed-circuit type of breathing apparatus used by frogmen in World War II prevented bubbles ascending to the surface, which might have been detected in enemy harbours, either visually or by sound-devices.

A Frenchman named Le Prieur designed a device in the 'thirties consisting of a tank of compressed air worn across the chest by a naked diver, and connected to a mouthpiece by a rubber hose. But he had to keep adjusting a valve every time he ascended or descended, and so precious air was wasted. Developing this invention, in 1942, Commandant J. Y. Cousteau and Emile Gagnan designed an automatic regulator which became the essential basis of the Aqualung system.

It supplied breathable air at any depth that the human body could endure. Le Prieur's apparatus could only be used down to depths of twelve or fifteen feet. Cousteau's first automatic compressed-air diving lung enabled him to go down to twenty-five feet. It was an oxygen rebreathing apparatus made from an oxygen cylinder, a gas-mask canister containing soda-lime, and a motor cycle inner tube. The gunsmith of the *Suffren*, on which Cousteau was serving, helped him to build it. The soda-lime filtered the carbon dioxide from the wearer's breath, and the equipment was worn on his back, the air-tube ending in the transparent face mask.

Cousteau continually improved the Aqualung in the

after years—he had been working on it since his pre-war skin-diving days, when (as Gunner Cousteau) he, Dumas and Taillez had formed a diving team. They had hunted fish with slingshots, spears and rubber-propelled harpoons, wearing no better underwater equipment than goggles.

On one occasion they gave Professor Piccard a shock. The adventurous three had watched the Professor descend on an experimental dive in his bathyscaphe. They waited until he had evidently reached a good depth, and then went down after him, wearing their goggles and foot fins and with a board, carried by one of them. They came upon the bathyscaphe at a depth of sixty feet and hovered for a few seconds in front of the observation window, displaying the board, on which these words were painted: "Come up when you want to!" Piccard said afterwards that it was one of the greatest surprises in all his underwater experiences.

Before the perfection of Cousteau's Aqualung only highly-trained experts could explore the coastal waters to any depth. But now, with but little cost and very little training, any swimmer can explore the waters, diving among the wonders of the sea unhampered by encumbering pipes or lines. The Aqualung wearer has no trouble with his eardrums, which are exposed to equal pressures —air within and water without. The air supply is adjusted to the diver's normal breathing rhythm. Control of the breathing can conserve the air, but it is never wasted in any case.

Seeing and breathing are provided for by separate devices. A mask covering part of the face, including the nose (to equalize pressure within the mask) is fitted with a glass eyeshield. The mouthpiece for breathing, held in the jaws, is separated from the mask for this reason: if the glass of the latter is broken the diver does not risk suffocation as with older types of mask. The diver in an Aqualung can breathe comfortably in any position, even upside-down. The fool-proof automatic valve takes care of everything.

Cousteau went to infinite trouble and experienced numerous periods of discomfort, risking his life on several occasions, to perfect the Aqualung and ensure the comfort and safety of its wearer.

On one occasion sailors from the *Suffren* rowed him out for a test of his equipment. This was in the earlier stages of its development and he had been given to understand that the depth-limit of the apparatus he was testing was forty-five feet. Cousteau went down to that depth, and then became interested in some fish, which seemed quite friendly. He saw a huge blue bream and followed it down beyond the safety limit, so engrossed in the fish that he forgot his own position. Suddenly, oxygen poisoning developed and his spine was bent back like a tensed bow. Just before he became unconscious he tore off the ten-pound weight he was carrying, and rose to the surface, where the sailors saw him floating and pulled him, still unconscious, into the boat.

He recovered after a painful few weeks of muscular trouble, and had scarcely regained his normal health when the war came. Later, transferred to Naval Intelligence at Marseilles, he was able to resume his experiments. He was soon working on the Fernez system, trying to improve on it. It was a simple type of apparatus, using a surface pump with an air line down to the diver. One day Cousteau was forty feet under water when the air tube broke. Dumas was even farther down—seventy-five feet below the surface. Cousteau saw his friend's air pipe rupture and knew that he was suffering a pressure treble that of the surface. The two men reached safety, but it was a near thing.

As time passed they went down to sixty, eighty and a hundred feet, and began to wonder what the boundary limit of their dives would be.

During the summer of 1943, using Cousteau's invention, he and his two friends were diving into the waters of the Mediterranean repeatedly. They and their families lived in a house near Marseilles. They carried out more than five hundred experiments with the Aqualung, and their underwater adventures then and since, recorded in a number of books and magazine articles, make fascinating reading. The day came when Dumas, testing his Aqualung, went deeper than any skin diver before him. Cousteau, from his "observation post" a hundred feet beneath the waves, watched him disappear. Dumas went down to two hundred and ten feet, and returned to the surface safe and happy—in his own words, "as merry as a bubble". Representing the greatest advance to date in diving equipment, the Aqualung has been used for years, safely and comfortably, as standard equipment of the British, French and U.S. Navies; also by shipping companies, life-guards, harbour commissions and cinema organizations. It is also used by the Universities of Washington, California, and Wisconsin, and many Fishery Investigations.

Salvage companies use them continually for heavy underwater work, and French submarine crews have used them successfully to escape from their vessels. Thousands of yachtsmen and sporting fishermen use them. Doing field work in a scarcely explored realm, marine biologists, archaeologists, hydrologists and other scientists find them invaluable. The police have used the services of local Aqualung owners on a number of occasions to recover bodies.

The ultimate depth to which divers will descend wearing Aqualungs is still a matter for conjecture. The countless investigations and experiments which have been made to date have revealed some sensational facts. Mankind lives and learns, and the barriers of yesterday are the easily-cleared hurdles of today. Dr. Halley, who sincerely believed (a little over two hundred years ago) that the absolute time limit of a diver's endurance under water was two minutes, would have said that it was impossible for a free-swimming diver to descend a hundred feet. But since his time scientists have found that the human body can stand greater underwater pressures than were once thought possible.

The human body is now believed to be no more compressible than that of a fish. Modern science tells us that a mammal may even be able to survive pressure equal to a depth of 450 feet, although no free-swimming diver had yet attained half that distance. Far below that record depth of 210 feet attained by Dumas in his Aqualung lies the world's record for the greatest descent ever made in a flexible diving-suit, encasing the human body: 535 feet attained by Petty Officer William Bolland, R.N., on 28th August 1948. He went down into the dark water equipped with one of Siebe, Gorman and Company's diving-suits and helium-oxygen apparatus, at Loch Fyne, Scotland. So the skin-divers have another 315 feet to go to equal the full-diving-suit limit.

Common-sense tells us that no skin-diver will ever reach such a depth. But the history of underwater exploration is one in which common-sense has frequently retreated, overwhelmed by the advancing tide of factual science.

Cousteau and his fellow fishmen have created a new realm of adventure in which almost anything can happen. The world's frogmen, contributing a vast accumulation of knowledge and experience to the new science of underwater exploration, endured hazards during their strange war-time activities which equalled the perils of their comrades far above them in the atmospheric ocean.

But peace-time provides the fishmen with adventures almost equally hazardous, and more humane—as when a group of divers may go down into the shore waters armed, not with explosives, but with implements for severing the stinging tentacles of certain jelly-fish for hospital research; or when Aqualung divers may help yachtsmen to recover their anchors; or perhaps assist technicians in laying electric cable across a river, with swift currents running, struggling with difficult tasks sixty or eighty feet below the surface.

Sunken vessels have provided sanctuary for countless myriads of fish since the first primitive ships made by man contributed some of their number, wrecked by gales or shattered on submerged reefs, to the treasures that rest on the world's sea-beds. For a number of centuries all kinds of sea creatures, lurking among the submerged wrecks, have been undisturbed by man. Thousands of sunken ships now rest on the ocean floors, their cabins and holds and state-rooms peopled by swimming, crawling and encrusting creatures. They hide in the nooks and corners of the wrecks, and feed on the corals and other marine growths that lie around or press upon the decaying hulks.

The fishmen are now evicting the fishes—sending them scuttling and writhing from the submerged decks, as they regain control of the ships and send up parts of them, and their cargoes, to the surface. Diving into the harbours and shore-waters of many countries, the fishmen go down, reclaiming mankind's lost property.

The divers are using electric scooters in some places to make explorations of sunken reefs. Huge sea-turtles turn aside as the scooters travel at three or four miles an hour through an element eight hundred times as dense and heavy as air. The electric scooters are bullet-shaped and can haul divers over considerable distances so that they experience little fatigue. What scenes they must see! The sea-beds of the shore-waters are seldom still—creatures burrow into them or break out of them: sometimes there are a number of upheavals in a limited area, like the eruptions of small volcanoes.

Plant-like animals cover the sunken rocks. Wrasse, groupers and squirrel-fish lurk under the coral. Tiny fish —red, yellow, green, blue and black—are everywhere along the reefs. Butterfly-fish move among the sponges and many-coloured sea-anemones: some of the sea-anemones, in thirty or forty feet of water, being as much as two feet across.

Numbers of colourful fish rest on branches and sprays of coral like birds in trees. Crustaceans of all kinds hide among the coral bases, like little land creatures among tree roots.

The wrecks are encrusted with coral growths. Sponges, oysters and other creatures cover the ship's bridges and wheelhouses and decks. Inside the more modern ones electric wires hang in festoons. Bottles, full and empty, swirl about with the motions of the sea or ride high under the encrusted ceilings. Everywhere chaos and decay are mercifully covered by the beauty of corals and under-water plants. In these sunken ships, costly chronometers, sextants, binoculars and other instruments, broken, corroded and ruined, lie about in the debris as if they were as valueless as the rotten pieces of wood or cordage upon which they rest.

Silent for so long, the waters within the wrecks may suddenly be alive with strange sounds. Quiescent for so long, save for the rippling movements of sea animals, the waters may suddenly be disturbed by violent concussions.

Down into the dark hold, into the submerged companion-ways, and through into the water-filled cabins, come these strange shapes—men with strange lumps on their backs and queer appendages hanging from their jaws. As they loom and recede, or set the submerged walls of the sunken ship shuddering with their knockings and scrapings, hosts of sea creatures swim to and fro in panic, or make for the outer sea.

After untold centuries the fishmen are entering the deeps—claiming the sea as their own.

CHAPTER X

TIGERS OF THE DEEP

WORKING twenty-five feet under water, on a coral reef midway between the Tuamota and Phoenix Islands, during the 1936 American Museum-Crocker Expedition to Tongareva (the name of the reef) Dr. Roy Waldo Miner was suddenly confronted with four sharks.

Wearing his underwater apparatus, Dr. Miner was otherwise naked and vulnerable, but he remembered some advice that had been given him by a native. Instead of retreating, he took several plunging steps towards the sharks, making violent swimming motions as he walked across the sea-bed. The sharks remained motionless for a few seconds and then turned and swam leisurely away, perhaps frightened a little by his menacing attitude. Dr. Miner returned to his work of photographing various creatures in the undersea gardens of the lagoon.

The crevices of the coral around him concealed many other perils. Dangerous moray eels, six or eight feet in length, lurked in the encrusted passages of the coral jungle. Sea-stars, immense creatures whose leathery bodies were covered with scarlet spines which were ball-socketed so that they could penetrate from many directions, crawled over the sea floor, sucking up animals through their powerful central mouths, as they crawled along, each using the countless tube feet on its sixteen arms to make progress. Swimming around Dr. Miner's head as he worked with his underwater camera, were all kinds of brightly coloured fishes.

He had learned by experience how to avoid or deal with most of the dangerous creatures of the lagoon bottom, and was afraid only of sharks. For as he said later, there is no infallible recipe for dealing with them. The native's advice was effective on that occasion, but, in Dr. Miner's own words, "Another day they might not be so accommodating."

In his account of this incident Dr. Miner, an intrepid and experienced explorer of the underseas, admits that he felt fear as the sharks approached him, but does not express an opinion one way or the other regarding this very debatable question: whether sharks will attack men except in self-defence. It is a problem which can only be examined properly if the views of experienced fishmen are compared, and this we shall do later in this chapter, after learning something of the shark's structure and habits.

In view of their enormous diversity fishes have been divided into numerous sub-classes and orders, but there are only three main divisions. These are, the *Cyclostomata* (fishes having pouched gills, the smallest of the three classes, comprising lampreys and hag-fishes); the *Teleostei*, which are the bony fishes; and the group *Selachii*, which includes the sharks and their allies.

The main difference between the *Selachii* and the other two classes is that sharks, rays and skates have a skeleton of cartilage or gristle, while the bony fishes have rigid, bony skeletons. Other differences are that the skin of a shark is covered by millions of tiny teeth. They actually *are* teeth—each one has its coating of enamel and its pulp cavity—so that they are rightly named "dermal denticles". They are microscopic compared with the shark's true teeth, but are extremely sharp. Each one is a scale with a sharp point projecting through the skin and attached to a plate in the dermis. These *placoid scales*, as they are termed, neither overlap nor touch one another. They are spaced in symmetrical rows with the utmost precision, and directed backwards. Sharkskin, commercially known as *shagreen* (although the term covers many kinds of grained leather prepared from the skins of animals, including wild asses, camels, sea-otters, and seals, besides sharks) is used in the manufacture of handbags, purses, spectacle-cases, etc.

Our own teeth are embedded in the bone of the jaw, but shark's true teeth (those in their mouths) are set in their gums. They may be sharply pointed and separate, or blunt and articulated together, so as to form pavement-like structures.

In some species the teeth roll over each other as the shark's mouth closes, like the cylinders in a crushing mill, producing a grinding effect of enormous power. The sharks known as the smooth hound, ray-toothed dog and skate-toothed varieties have these peculiar grinders, which are rendered necessary by the food on which they live: such as hard-shelled molluscs and crustaceans, whose armour is ground under the bony rollers.

Sharks' teeth resemble those of the whelk in the fact that they are replaceable, but while the whelk has its teeth on a ribbon the shark's are individually renewable. Each tooth has other teeth beneath it, so that a continuous succession is provided for every tooth as it wears away or breaks off. A single tooth may be renewed more than a hundred times in a shark's lifetime. One might think that because the teeth are set in the creature's gums they would not be so strong as if fixed in their jaws; but there cannot be much wrong with the arrangement considering that sharks can bite through steel hawsers and tear the flesh of dead whales to ribbons as though they had been ripped by circular saws.

The white shark's teeth form one of the most extraordinary structures possessed by any animal for tearing and grinding its food. Crocodiles and other creatures can renew their teeth, but the white shark is far more efficient. If the shark is an adult it has in its upper and lower jaw six rows of renewable teeth, and these can take different motions according to the will of the animal. It has an arsenal of fearsome weapons for the destruction of its victims and enemies, and it uses them economically.

The rows of teeth are obedient to the muscles round their bases, by means of which the shark can erect or retract any of its rows in accordance with its requirements. It can even erect a portion of a row, while the rest remain depressed in their beds. Thus the tyrant of the ocean can measure the number and power of its weapons and use the requisite rows or parts of rows. For the destruction of the weak and defenceless one row of teeth may suffice. As it snatches at its prey it may be in such a position that certain rows of teeth are better placed to deal with it. For formidable adversaries it can bring its entire arsenal into play.

It has other offensive weapons. It can use its skin aggressively and effectively. Its tail is possessed of immense power and is capable of breaking a man's arm or leg in one swift lashing stroke.

The shark again differs from the bony fishes in that it has no air-bladder; while it is distinguished from the rays and skates of its own group by the position of its branchial clefts, which are always lateral, by its fan-shaped pectoral fins, which (with few exceptions) have restricted bases, and by the shape of its body, which is rounded and elongated and which tapers to its tail. This is heterocercal—unequally lobed.

Sharks breathe by gill-sacs or pouches, which open externally on the neck by gill-slits, of which there are from five to seven pairs. Water may also be admitted through the spiracles: a pair of openings on the upper side of the head which contain a rudimentary gill, and communicate with the mouth.

The majority of sharks are viviparous, and in some the embryos are nourished in a placenta-like structure. Those that are oviparous, like the dogfish, which is usually

selected as typical of the *Elasmobranchii* (the sharks most
nearly resembling bony fish), lay their eggs in capsules
or cases of horny material, within which the embryos are
protected. The dogfishes are spread over most of the
temperate and tropical seas. They lay oblong eggs. At
each corner of the egg a long thread is attached, and
these serve to fasten the eggs to fixed objects. Those of
some of the tropical species are beautifully ornamented
and coloured. The two British species of the dogfish shark
—the lesser and the larger spotted dogfish—belong to the
most common fishes around our coasts, and are often
confused with each other. The latter (which may attain
a length of four feet) may be identified by its larger
rounded spots, which are merely dots in the lesser kind.

During the mating season, the males and females of
the viviparous sharks seek each other and approach the
coasts, in pairs, forgetting their ferocity for a time. The
eggs are hatched at intervals in the female's oviducts;
and the little ones issue two or three at a time. As soon
as it is born the shark becomes the scourge of the sea.
It eats all kinds of molluscs and fishes, cod-fish, flounders,
cuttle-fish—almost anything that swims or crawls in the
sea. Yet if it has been feeding well for a time it will discriminate. Sometimes, if hungry, it will eat the carcasses
of men and sea-creatures—at other times it will spurn
them.

Some writers insist that sharks discriminate regarding
human food, preferring white to yellow men and both
to the negro. Whatever their tastes in the under-waters—
where they may or may not attack divers—they certainly make ferocious attacks on any humans when they
meet them on the surface. They will follow ships for
miles, greedily swallowing any food thrown to them or
dumped overboard, and immediately attack any persons
who fall into the sea. They have been known to leap into
boats when attacking fishermen, and one account
describes how a shark hurled itself into the air and

snapped its jaws within a few inches of the corpse of a negro, suspended from a yard-arm twenty feet above the sea's surface.

Many authorities say that because a shark's mouth is placed in the lower part of its head, it becomes necessary for it to turn over on its back before it can seize any swimmer on the surface; and that natives, knowing this habit of the shark, take advantage of it and plunge their knives into the killers as they turn. But other authorities claim that the shark is too shrewd to make itself vulnerable by any such action, and point out that it continually devours creatures of the sea-beds while remaining in a normal position, with its mouth pressed downward. The truth may be a compromise between the two viewpoints. Sharks certainly *do* turn over as they attack—but not always.

The white shark—known the world over as the man-eater—is white below and brown on its upper parts. It is almost a stranger to Britain's shores, but stray specimens sometimes appear, particularly in hot summers. This is one of the largest sharks that range the oceans, and in some seas they are so numerous that they are the terror of natives and sailors. One specimen, whose jaws are still preserved, measured no less than thirty-seven feet in length. Specimens twenty feet long are fairly common.

This tiger of the deep is rivalled, in its destructive habits, by the blue shark—another monster that has earned the name of man-eater. It is slaty-blue on its upper, and white on its under parts. Exceedingly destructive to shoals of food-fishes, it will pursue them even into fishermen's nets.

The thresher shark, another variety, ranges from twelve to fifteen feet in length, and is known by its elongated upper tail lobe. This it uses to stun and kill hosts of smaller fish—numbers of threshers suddenly rushing into a school of them and herding their victims into a mulling panic-stricken circle as they furiously flail

187

them before darting in and devouring them in enormous numbers.

Having teeth somewhat different from other sharks, the five species known as hammerheads, or hammer-headed sharks, form a group unique among fishes, in view of the extraordinary conformation of the head. Instead of retaining its usual more or less pointed form, the front part of the head of these sharks is broadened and expanded on each side to form a hammer-like (or more accurately, mallet-like) structure.

There is nothing in the habits of the creature that accounts for its strange shape. The eyes of this shark are placed at either end of the projecting extremities, and are therefore abnormally wide apart, so that the hammerhead's bifocal vision must give it a remarkable impression of all that it sees. The mouth is set centrally and between the two projections, so that its corners coincide with a line drawn centrally through them.

The hammerhead produces its young alive. From the interior of a very fine specimen, captured near Tenby in 1839, which measured more than ten feet in length, thirty-nine young ones—all perfectly formed and averaging nineteen inches in length—were taken. The flesh of the hammerhead is hard, coarse and uneatable, but that of some sharks is very palatable.

All over the world—in the United States, China, India and other places—shark fisheries have developed in recent decades for the purpose of securing and marketing the twenty-one products which can be obtained from the bodies of sharks. For centuries the animal had been regarded as a loathsome creature with disgusting habits which made it a pariah and an outcast with no redeeming features, commercial or otherwise. According to travellers' accounts it was a cannibalistic brute—devouring its own babies; a gross and filthy feeder; a treacherous killer—Nature had certainly gone crazy in creating the shark: a verminous abortion that was no use to man. But advancing science has shown many of the accounts to be old wives' tales, and numbers of the "facts" collected about the shark mere superstitious fancies.

In some Eastern countries the natives used the fins as food and considered them delicacies—but the flesh was regarded as worthless and only fit for the very poorest classes. Certain peoples of the South Seas, it is true, covered the handles of their weapons and oars with sharkskin—but no attempts were made to cure the material properly, so that it was thought to be unfit for much else, being dry and hard.

The scientist Dr. Ehrenreich was one of the first to change all this. His researches in the early part of the present century have contributed towards turning what was regarded as a worthless scavenger of the seas into a benefactor of mankind, for he showed that every particle of a shark's carcass has some commercial value. Today, sharkskin leather is barely distinguishable from any other. It is in fact far stronger than cowhide and much more durable. Strands of sharkskin are longer than those of cowhide, and the leather from some species can be split into as many as fourteen layers without depreciation of its qualities. The soft skins of unborn sharks make an excellent substitute for doeskin.

The shagreen often seen on cigarette boxes and other articles has been specially treated. The "teeth" have to be removed—those tiny scales already mentioned, which are so tough that no needle can penetrate them—before the leather can be used for articles which have to be handled. Shark meat, once regarded as almost uneatable, is now consumed in thousands of tons by civilized peoples, few of whom realize what they are eating. In London alone, before the last war, nearly two thousand tons of shark meat was eaten annually. Some of it was of the dried variety from sharks, but most of it came from the dogfish. It is probably being consumed in even greater quantities today in most cities and towns of this country, and in all parts of the world, and has the popular name of "rock salmon". But the phrase "shark and chips" has not yet become colloquial.

Another highly important product of the shark fisheries is shark oil. Most of it is extracted from the fish's liver, yet many of the encyclopaedias published in the nineteenth century described the liver of the shark not merely as "uneatable" but as "very poisonous". Much of the oil is used for mixing with cod liver oil—not as an adulterant but because shark oil contains twice as much iodine as any other, so that cod liver oil is greatly improved by its addition. As much as eighteen gallons of oil have been obtained from the liver of a single shark. The oil is also used in many other ways—for cooking purposes, in leather dressing, and as a lubricant, etc. The liver itself is ground into poultry food. Apart from the liver, the flesh of sharks yields an extract which compares favourably with extract of beef for nutritive purposes.

Dyes of many kinds are manufactured from sharks' bodies. The bones are ground up to make meal for cattle and chickens. Glue is yet another substance that comes from their carcasses. Some idea of the value of the shark in the world's markets may be gained from the fact that the shark-fin trade of other nations with China alone, in prewar times, necessitated the capturing of over a hundred thousand sharks annually.

Skates and rays are among the most hideous and repulsive of all fish. Some of them attain enormous dimensions, while many are dangerous because of the wounds inflicted by the spines of their tails. The true rays lead a sedentary life, moving slowly over the floors of the sea-shelves and seldom rising to the surface. The tail of the ray has almost entirely lost its function as an organ of locomotion—it acts as a simple rudder. The fish progresses by means of its pectoral fin, which maintains an undulating motion. Nearly all rays lay eggs. Many of them ascend rivers to a considerable distance.

The thornback is a common ray in the coastal waters of Great Britain, and is taken plentifully along our shores. It is so called from the number of thorny projections scattered over its back and along its spine.

Known also by the sinister name of devil-fishes, the eagle rays include some of the largest representatives of their tribe, and are characterized by their flatness and extreme width. The tail is slender and whip-like, the mouth-cleft straight, and the teeth, when present, form a mosaic or pavement, perfectly adapted for crushing the shells of molluscs and other hard substances. The teeth are arranged in seven longitudinal rows, those of the unpaired middle row being much elongated, while the other rows form irregular hexagons. Some of the fossils of this genus show that the living creatures of prehistoric times must have had tusks five inches in length. Our modern ones may attain a length of ten feet and weigh several hundredweights. When captured these eagle rays lash out fiercely with their tails, the spines of which may inflict considerable damage.

But there are even bigger devil-fishes. The largest existing members of the family belong to the genera *Dicerobatis* and *Cephaloptera*, and are mainly confined to the tropical seas. In the former the pectoral fins do not extend to the sides of the head, which is cut away in front and furnished with a pair of appendages which are directed forward, like horns, the nostrils being widely separated, so that the creature's appearance is certainly devilish. One of the Indian representatives of this genus is known to measure eighteen feet across its disc, while a weight of 1,200 pounds—over half a ton—has been recorded. Sir W. Eliot, who gave special study to this fish, stated that the horn-like appendages "are used by the animal to draw its prey into its mouth, which opens like a huge cavern between them. The fishermen in India say they see these creatures swimming slowly along with their mouths open, and flapping these great sails (the fin-rays) inwards, drawing in the smaller crustaceans on which they feed".

There seems to be hardly any limit to the size of this creature. Reading through numbers of accounts of them, their dimensions are given again and again as "the largest known"—and then exceeded again and again in further accounts. One authority says "Swimmers very often perish in them, or at best lose an arm or a leg". There can be no doubt that humans have often been bitten in two by these devil-fish, with their terrible triangular teeth, roughly 144 in number and furnished with saw-like edges.

A French naturalist, M. le Vaillant, was a passenger in a sailing-ship towards the end of the last century, crossing the warm waters of the Mediterranean, when he saw three of these huge fish sporting around the ship. After some persuasion the captain was induced to order his crew to effect their capture. They secured what M. le Vaillant later described as "the smallest of the three". When it was brought on board it was found to measure twenty-eight feet in width, and to weigh over a ton. Its mouth was easily large enough to swallow a full-grown man.

Despite their ferocity the male and female devil-fish show the utmost affinity towards each other and will defend their little ones with their lives. It has happened on numbers of occasions that one fish has been harpooned or otherwise fatally wounded, and its mate has hung about the boat until it shared the same fate. In one instance where the female had been caught in a tunny net, a male devil-fish was seen wandering about the net for days and was at last found dead in the partition of the net where his mate had been captured, although her body had been removed. The sentimental words used by the authority who records this story—"the name devil-fish ought not to be applied to so loving and faithful a creature"—may have some semblance of sense.

(Black Star)

odds against getting the above photograph with an ordinary ("still") camera were a ...ion to one. After watching porpoises playing in the Caribbean for several hours, the ...ographer suddenly snapped this seven-foot monster as it leaped into the air. Below: ...her spectacular leap—by a salmon, on the River Tummel in Perthshire; indicating the amazing muscular power of these fish.

(Picture Post Library)

*Jack and the porpoise.
"Take it quickly enough
and you can have it."*

(Black Star)

Another ferocious member of the shark group is the sting ray, called in some places the fire flaire, on account of the bright red colour of the flesh when the fish is cut open. These are some of the most specialized members of the entire group. The pectoral fins are continued right round the extremity of the muzzle, so that they form the entire margin of the fish. In the centre of its very wide disc the head and body are elevated. The typical genus contains no fewer than twenty-five species of sting rays, but the term should be restricted to those species with armed tails. These tails are long, flexible and whip-like, and even if they had no stings they could inflict a sharp vicious blow like the cut of a horse-whip. But the destructive efficiency of the weapon is increased by its projecting spine, extremely sharp at the point and double-edged: each edge being furnished with a series of razor-keen teeth. When the sting ray is attacked or even disturbed it can use this frightful weapon with such strength and rapidity that the flesh of its victim can be lashed to ribbons. Owing to the fact that aggravated inflammation often follows wounds caused by the sting ray in hot countries, the notion prevails among native peoples that the creature's tail is supplied with poison, and some modern reference works perpetuate this error. But there is no poisonous substance in the tail—any inflammation in wounds caused by it is due to other factors, such as unsterilized dressings.

Some of the savage inhabitants of the Pacific Islands have used the sting ray's barb in the past as a barb for their own weapons. Affixed to a shaft it makes one of the cruellest weapons ever fashioned by man. For its chief merit in the eyes of the savages who have used it has not merely been the terrible wounds it inflicts but the fact that the jagged blade is practically certain to snap asunder at the point where it enters the body of a foe, leaving the barb in the wound: its peculiar shape ensuring that it is virtually impossible to get it out again.

The electric rays (family *Torpedinidae*) are the most curious and mysterious members of the ray group. In common with the electric eel (*Gymnotus*) and the African catfish (*Malapterurus*) it has the power of benumbing or even killing its victims by delivering electric shocks. The electric ray is represented by several genera, ranging over the Mediterranean Sea and the Atlantic and Indian Oceans, and is otherwise known as the cramp-fish, the cramp ray, the numb-fish and the torpedo.

Dr. Albert Günther (1830–1914), the German-born zoologist who, as a naturalized British subject was the keeper of the British Museum's zoological department for twenty years, exhaustively investigated the strange power possessed by these fishes. He wrote: "The fish gives the electric shock voluntarily, when it is excited to do so in self-defence, or intends to stun or kill its prey; but to receive the shock the object must complete the galvanic circuit by communicating with the fish at two distinct points, either directly or through the medium of some conducting body. If an insulated frog's leg touches the fish, by the end of the nerve only, no muscular contractions ensue on the discharge of the battery, but a second point of contact immediately produces them. It is said that a painful sensation may be produced by a discharge conveyed through the medium of a stream of water. The electric currents created in these fishes exercise all the known properties of electricity: they render the needle magnetic, decompose chemical compounds, and emit the spark."

The torpedo is slow in its movements, quite unlike its fellow ray the devil-fish, with its lightning-like lashing movements. Without its power to use electricity as a weapon it could not catch the swift and active fishes on which it feeds. It has its mysterious power completely under control. It does not always deliver the shock. If it is not irritated or angered it may be touched and even handled—contacting it at the two points which would in other circumstances cause the discharge of electricity—without inflicting a shock. But if it is repeatedly irritated or teased the discharge inevitably occurs. The shock varies considerably in its effect on different individuals. Fishermen may be made aware of the fact that they have a torpedo in their meshes by a sudden shock through their arms and chests as they are hauling in a net. An angler may receive a discharge of electricity if the line he is holding is wet and if it fouls one of the creatures.

In one particular experiment with a torpedo it was placed in a vessel of water with a live duck, which at first swam around without touching it. The torpedo became excited, moved towards the duck and contacted it—and the bird was instantly killed. A writer in *Land and Water* in 1869, replying to Buckland the noted zoologist, observed: "I have taken two torpedoes in the estuary of the Tees. You say the one you dissected had nothing in its stomach. I was curious to see what those I caught were living upon, so I put my knife into one, and took from him an eel 2 lbs. in weight, and a flounder nearly 1 lb. The next one I opened also, and was astonished to find in him a salmon between 4 and 5 lbs. weight: and what I was more astonished at was that none of the fish had a blemish of any description, showing that your idea of the fish killing his prey with his electrical force is quite correct."

Experiments have shown that the upper surface of the torpedo corresponds with the copper plate of a simple battery, and the lower surface with the zinc plate. Among numerous experiments which have been conducted with electric fishes, one of the most remarkable was that of Professor Ewart, who demonstrated the fact that the common Skate—not included among electric fishes but nevertheless a member of the Shark group—possessed a rudimentary electric organ and could produce faint electrical discharges.

It has been shown that all the electric organs of the

torpedoes, catfish and electric eels are modified muscle-tracts. The associated nerve-endings are comparable to the normal terminations of the motor nerves on muscles. But this fact contributes nothing whatever to the solution of the problem. Nor does the structure of the muscle-tracts shed the slightest light on the question: How do these electric fishes produce and control their electrical currents? The organs consist of a very large number of rounded columns or chambers, each enclosed in a thin membrane.

The entire structure is duplex. The columns are separated by longitudinal and transverse partitions of fibrous connective tissues. The nerves taper to extreme thinness, branch considerably, and finally fuse with what may be described as "plates" or "discs" of modified muscular substance. Each of the columns or prismatic chambers contains a jelly-like substance or fluid.

A rough model of the structure might be made by making a number of piles of coins, with attenuated bladders between them—in fact a kind of "voltaic" group of piles. The length of the columns, and consequently the number of discs in the various piles, varies according to their position in the creature's body. The columns extend right through the creature's body, from the skin of the back to that of the abdomen, and are clearly visible on both sides, so that those in the middle of the animal are necessarily the longest and those at either end are much shorter piles of discs.

In some large specimens of the electric fishes as many as eleven hundred columns have been counted. A vast amount of blood is circulated through its electric organ, and the structure is permeated with complicated mazes of nerves which run in every direction—far more complex than any telephone switchboard's wires. How the discs in the structure come to be charged with electricity is still a mystery to which science has not yet provided the complete answer.

Wiedersheim and Parker have stated: "The side of the electric plate on which the nerve branches out is negative at the moment of discharge, while the opposite side is positive." (This refers to each disc in the structure.) "From the different arrangements of the parts the electric shock passes in different directions in the three fishes. In *Malapterurus* (the catfish) from the head to the tail; in *Gymnotus* (the electric eel) in the contrary direction; in the torpedo from below upwards."

The organ's activity is entirely dependent upon two factors—the nerve stimulus from the brain of the creature, when it wills to send out an electrical discharge, and a certain degree of freshness in the structure itself. If the nerve connections with the brain are severed there can be no discharge—showing that it is not just a "battery". Also, if the animal is tired, or there have been repeated discharges, the power to produce the current temporarily ceases.

It is a remarkable fact that the torpedo, gifted with such exceptional power among fishes, should have one tiny foe which is quite insensible to electric shocks. This is the *Branchellion*, a parasitic creature classified with the *Hirudinea* (leeches), which generally measures from an inch to an inch and a half in length. It clings to the torpedo and feeds upon its juices, yet remains completely indifferent to its host's electrical discharges. The currents must pass through this tiny creature's body, yet discharges which are enough to kill fishes thousands of times larger than *Branchellion* leave it quite unharmed.

The remora, or sucking-fish—a popular name for any species of the family *Echineididae* and order *Discocephali*—is a parasitic fish of a different kind, averaging two feet in length, which specializes in its attachments to various creatures larger than itself. Some confine themselves to dolphins, some to swordfish, and so on. The common species on the Atlantic coast of the United States is the shark-sucker (*Echineis naucrates*), which is usually found fixed to sharks, although it may be found attached to a few other species. It seems to be a completely worthless fish, for it has no food value and yields no commercial products. Yet men have found a use for it.

When Columbus, the year after his first voyage of discovery, returned to the Caribbean, he lingered among the south coast islets, which he named "the Gardens of the Queen" and watched the Indians using the remora as a fishing device. They fastened cords to the tails of remoras, threw them into the sea, and waited until they attached themselves to larger fishes, which were then hauled ashore. Columbus saw them haul in a huge turtle, with the sucking-fish still clinging to it.

The remora's peculiarity, making it in the words of one authority the "hitch-hiker of the sea", is its dorsal fin, which is at first like those of other fishes, but changes during its lifetime into a complex sucker, shaped like the sole of a shoe. This gives it a powerful hold on any object or creature to which it attaches itself. It hangs on to larger fishes until a meal is reached, which it shares with its host and then digests as it is carried along. If it feels that its host (being replete) is not likely to provide it with another meal for a while, it will detach itself and look around for another fish in a hungrier condition. Yet it does not seem to have any power of discrimination between living and dead things, and will fasten itself to the hull of a ship as firmly as to a shark's belly.

There are many old legends and historical accounts which indicate that the ancients believed in the remora's power of arresting and detaining ships in full sail through their power of suction. Mark Antony's galley in the battle of Actium was said to have been held fast by a group of remoras, which defied the efforts of several hundred men to free the vessel. Some old writers give the name "reversus" to the sucker-fish, from the erroneous idea that the creature swims upside-down. As it clings to a bigger fish or object it may sometimes give that impression, but it actually swims in the normal position.

It is a curious fact that the inherent laziness of the sucking-fish should be linked with a form of laziness in man—for using them to capture other fish is probably the least strenuous way of capturing the creatures of the sea. The Caribbean Indians—unlike the fishermen of China, Australia and other parts—treat remoras as pets—even as intimate friends. Before and after their hunting trips they talk freely with their remoras, encouraging them, cajoling them, and praising them; fully believing that the animals are intelligent and can understand every word they say, and that they like being caressed and praised for their (entirely passive) efforts.

Some of mankind's strangest customs and habits are connected with sharks and their near relatives. Off the Canary Islands, for instance, the naked divers once used a peculiar method of disarming the stinging ray. The native would go down into the water without a weapon when he had learned that a stinging ray lurked upon the sea-bed near the shore, and would watch his opportunity, circling the venomous creature, and then suddenly dart in and bite off the formidable sting just above the jagged blade. Deprived of its weapon, the fish would lash its tail in fury, but could be safely lassoed and hauled to the surface.

The period from 1925 to 1928 was a time of shark activity in the world's oceans which was probably greater than any corresponding period for many centuries—certainly it has not been equalled since. Innumerable cases of the capture of out-sized sharks in most of the world's shore-waters were reported, and there were many cases of fierce struggles between human beings and the killers.

Attacks by sharks of exceptional size had been increasing in the years immediately prior to the period. To take but one of the earlier instances, recorded at the time by

Mitchell-Hedges, the famous explorer, big-game hunter and fisherman:

According to the London *Daily Express* dated 15th June 1922, Mitchell-Hedges had been on an expedition to South America since the previous December, and was preparing to go to Panama via Kingston, Jamaica, when he received news that a white girl of 15, Miss Adlin Lopez, had been killed by a shark at Kingston. The message begged him to stop there on his journey and capture the monster.

The child had been bathing in Kingston Harbour with a little boy of five. She was standing alone, in four feet of water near a small wooden pier, when she suddenly shrieked "Father! Father! Help me!" Her father rushed to her and found that her leg had been cut off at the thigh as though by a razor. She told him she had felt no pain, "only a tickling sensation", before she fainted in his arms. Next day the girl died in a nearby hospital.

It was estimated that the pressure required to sever a limb close to the body in that way, in a single snap, would require a strength in the shark's jaws equivalent to a pressure of one and a half tons. Mitchell-Hedges made his preparations to capture the shark. He attached five lines to gasoline drums and moored the drums to the bottom with an iron weight. He baited the lines with massive pieces of meat.

His first attempt was quickly successful in attracting the shark, showing that it had been lurking near the shore, with its appetite only whetted, awaiting another meal. It struck at one of the baits, and the sea around was immediately thrown into a state of turbulence as the shark lashed and struggled among the bobbing drums. A huge crowd assembled on the beach and watched the shark's efforts to free itself of the great steel hook. With a final convulsive snap it actually buckled the great steel hook, tearing its barb off—but too late to escape.

This shark, a female, was abnormal in many ways. Although only eleven feet long its girth was nearly nine feet. It carried three young ones, nearly ready to be born. It had a double fracture of its backbone, which nature had repaired by forming a large cylindrical growth around the affected part. Experts reached the conclusion that the shark was insane—insanity is by no means confined to humans—through its injuries and other malformations. So the incident ended: the shark paying for killing the child with the loss of its own life and the prenatal deaths of its young.

Between 1922 and 1925 sharks appeared along the world's coastlines in increasing numbers.

Early in 1925 they began to invade Britain's home waters. The *Daily Chronicle*, referring to a report that sharks had been seen in Carmarthen Bay, told its readers that they had no cause for alarm, and reminded them that "there are sharks and sharks". It went on: "150 different species have been described. Those found in temperate latitudes are quite unlike the tiger sharks and man-eaters of the tropics." It admitted that sharks frequenting home waters became troublesome to fishermen on rare occasions, by taking their bait and driving away fish, but this kind of shark was "comparatively harmless".

The *Birmingham Weekly Post* of 2nd May recorded the capture of "the heaviest skate ever caught", at Brighton a few days before. "It weighs," the paper declared, "250 lbs., or 50 lb. more than the naturalists of a century ago thought it ever attained."

The *Post* writer then added a fact or two which made the weight seem insignificant, giving an account of a devil-fish "caught in 1823" which "weighed nearly five tons" and was so monstrous that "three pairs of oxen, one horse and 22 men all pulling together could not convey it far".

Only two days later a spectacular fight occurred between a shark and a porpoise in the Firth of Clyde, ending in the death of the porpoise after the shark had bitten off its tail. Such fights are certainly not common around British coasts.

Sharks, rays and skates appeared in various places during ensuing weeks, until on 25th July a large sting ray weighing over forty pounds was caught in the West End bathing pool, West Park, Jersey, after killing a young man named Gould.

Only the day before a large sting ray weighing slightly less—thirty-six pounds—was captured and killed by boys fishing in the Solent off Yarmouth. They were fortunate in their avoidance of the ray's barbed weapon.

Around this time, a member of the crew of the *Royal Sovereign* lightship, seven miles off Eastbourne, angling for congers, hooked a shark of the man-eating variety. He and other men hauled it aboard the lightship, after it had fought fiercely in the water. A man had been bitten by a shark near Weymouth, some time before this, without serious injury, and a ten-foot hammerhead had been caught in Carmarthen Bay.

Bathers around Britain were alarmed throughout the 1925 summer by the appearance of sharks and stinging rays in numerous places. As late as October that year a huge shark was caught off Lyme Regis, Dorset, by some fishermen in a boat about a mile from shore. The two men had a desperate struggle with the man-killer before they were able to dispatch it and haul it into their boat. A little later the catch of a drifter which reached Ramsgate—the vessel had been fishing for herrings—included no fewer than thirty sharks, some of them of considerable size. So it went on through the summers of 1926, 1927 and 1928. On the South Wales coast the 1927 summer was a record one for sharks—six were caught at Porthcawl, fourteen in Swansea Bay, and twelve in Carmarthen Bay.

During these years sharks were killing numbers of

bathers in all parts of the world—and men were killing sharks.

On 18th February 1928, the largest shark ever caught on rod and line was landed by Mr. H. White-Wickham of London—a gargantuan thresher which he fought for hours at Whangaroa, New Zealand. The *Auckland Weekly News* published a photograph of Mr. White-Wickham standing beside his extraordinary catch. On the fish, figures were painted showing its weight: 832 lb.— nearly seven and a half hundredweights.

All these accounts—which might be supplemented *ad infinitum* by others, describing battles with man-killing monsters during those years and since, in the shore-waters of all countries—are concerned with the activities of sharks on the surface. They give us no impression of a harmless fish that might be scared away by splashing motions of the arms and legs. But (as some writers on skin-diving and underwater exploration firmly assert) it may be that the shark's attitude towards man is very different when it meets him several fathoms down, or on the sea-bed itself.

We have now learned enough of the shark's structure and habits to enable us to examine some of the statements made by fishmen regarding this controversial question: Is the shark harmless in the underwater regions if left alone and not attacked by divers?

The *Encyclopaedia Britannica* describes some varieties as "dangerous" or "very dangerous" to man, but—in common with many other reference works—states that the basking shark is "quite harmless unless attacked". *Chambers's Encyclopaedia* says that some of the larger forms "sometimes devour men who swim incautiously in warm seas"—but does not make it clear whether this applies to surface or underwater swimming.

Captain Jacques-Yves Cousteau, universally recognized as the leading authority on underwater exploration and co-inventor of the Aqualung, has definite ideas about sharks. In an article in the *National Geographic Magazine* for October 1952 he describes one of his numerous meetings with them. He is the leader of the 1951–52 expedition, on the *Calypso*, into the Mediterranean and Red Seas; has reached the objective of his voyage—the island of Abu Latt—and is "down under" in the coral kingdom clad only in goggles, trunks and flippers. (The compressors they had been using for Aqualung diving were temporarily out of order.) Underwater with him are Professor Pierre Drach, Wladimir Nesteroff, the biologist, and Dr. de la Brunière. Suddenly a five-foot shark catches sight of the four men and rushes towards them at terrific speed.

"Fortunately," writes Cousteau, "when he was only three feet away, the shark slued around at twenty to thirty knots and shot away. I did not wait for him to make a second pass. I retreated to the barge." Cousteau, safe above the surface, pondered the way the shark had upset not merely their peace of mind but some of their preconceptions about sharks. "*First*, this fish had seen us from as far away as we had seen him. His eyesight, or some other sense, must have been very keen to permit him to find my position instantly. *Second*, he had attacked deliberately, at great speed, though we had expected sharks, in these coastal waters, to be very cautious. *Third*, he had veered away sharply and rapidly at a moment when I was making a frantic and probably futile effort to get out of his line of attack. In brief, he could hardly be said to have manœuvred poorly, as we had often been told."

He goes on to describe his relations with sharks in the weeks that followed. He says that sudden gestures would drive them away, but they would quickly return; that if the divers turned their backs on them the sharks would swoop at their legs at once; that if they faced the creatures and swam in their direction the sharks would retreat—but only for a while; so that Cousteau and his colleagues decided that the important thing to do was to gain time and get out of the water at the first opportunity.

When they had regained their Aqualungs they went down to one hundred and sixty feet, into what Cousteau describes as "the sharks' merry-go-round", photographing the creatures and their surroundings. Below them sharks were wandering over the sand shoal. Above them, silhouetted against the shining surface, the long dark shadows of the sharks moved menacingly. Watching the ferocious beasts swimming around his naked companions, who now included Dumas (whose ankles were actually sniffed at by an enormous shark before Cousteau hooted loudly through his mouthpiece and drove it away) Cousteau reflected on the strange scene, and could only conclude—in the words of his article—that they were all mad.

His final conclusion on the matter was that sharks are cowards—ferocious cowards, but still cowards—and that they look upon the diver as a strange bubble-blowing fish with two tails—"worth investigating but not quite safe to charge".

Cornel Lumière, an explorer, both of the world's land and sea surfaces and of the under-waters as a diver and swimmer, regards sharks as harmless unless attacked. In his book *Beneath the Seven Seas** he says: "Once I belonged to the timids who visualize a shark stuffed with human arms and legs, every time they see a few feet of ocean. It took a little time and some special effort, but I now share the ranks of those who maintain that it is a good deal safer to play round with a shark under water than with a blonde on Broadway." He adds that if you leave a shark alone he will leave you alone, and adds: "Read Hass, Craig, Cousteau and they will tell you, unless you provide specific attractions for the shark, he will not come near you."

Lumière says that "of some forty varieties of sharks,

*Hutchinson & Co. Ltd., 1956.

only one is classified as a man-eater", and gives its name: the White Shark. One need go no further than the *Encyclopaedia Britannica* to find that "altogether some hundred and fifty species have been described", with references to many of them as dangerous. But Lumière defines the conditions under which they may be dangerous, and is no doubt right regarding the sharks he has met personally. He says that sharks will certainly attack if they smell blood. "If you hurt yourself on a coral-head," he writes, "or otherwise, and are bleeding, go into the boat until it stops. If a fish you shoot is bleeding badly, get the bloody thing in the boat fast!" He goes on to say that most of the sharks met with close to the shore are sand sharks, and cowards. But his statement that "no shark will stand up to you if you swim to meet him" seems a little sweeping. He has admitted that the white shark is a man-eater—and there are evidently many huge sharks outside Lumière's experience which it would be insane folly to approach.

Regarding rays, Lumière makes some remarkable statements. He says: "Rays are colourful and pleasant playmates to the spearman." They have no mean streak in them, he declares, so that "you may touch them safely if you feel so inclined". He says regarding sting rays that he actually touched them, yet in no instance did they even try to strike: "Once I was surrounded by half a dozen of these graceful creatures while they were executing a perfect underwater ballet."

Lumière has an interesting reference to the noted fishman Hans Hass whom he describes as "moving about amongst sharks and patting them with a fatherly hand".

Towards the end of his book he makes two further references to sharks. In the first of these he tells us that Cupric acetate has been discovered to be the most effective shark repellent, and that it is now standard equipment in the U.S. Navy and Air Force life-jackets. In his final reference (p. 223) he asks "How harmless are nurse sharks?" These are the dogfishes—sharks quite distinct from the white shark, described earlier by Lumière as being the only dangerous variety. He answers his own question in these words: "Two young, but experienced, divers in Puerto Rico required a combined score of twenty-five stitches to close up wounds inflicted upon them by a shark less than five feet long. The little nurse shark weighed only 35 lb." Nurse sharks (or dogfishes) are among the most abundant sharks found in shore-waters.

John Sweeney in *Skin Diving and Exploring Underwater**
attributes all danger from sharks to fear. He says (p. 123): "Fear of the unknown, the dark muddy depths, the black inside of a wreck, the creepy light under a wharf, or the ghoulish arena of lake water, must be recognized for what it is and cast aside." He declares that "many divers, even with years of experience, still fear sharks. This is principally because they have read fanciful books and articles by writers who have never had an encounter with a shark".

Some might query Mr. Sweeney's statement and point out that most divers would be inclined to trust their own personal knowledge of sharks in preference to any gained from fanciful books and articles.

Mr. Sweeney, in the same page, makes what is probably the most extraordinary statement ever made by a writer on the world's oceans. He says: "There is nothing to harm you under the surface of the sea. You take more chances on a Sunday-afternoon drive in your car than you do swimming leisurely underwater." Some of us will still hold to our opinions that men like Cousteau, Lumière, Hass, Drach, Dumas and Doukan—to mention only a few of the fishmen—need more courage than Sunday-afternoon car drivers.

Marcel Isy-Schwart, an undersea explorer who has killed hundreds of ferocious sea creatures, says in *Hunting*

*Frederick Muller Ltd., 1956.

Big Fish:* "Underwater hunting is evidently not a sport without risks." He gives accounts of many of his fights with big fish, and says of the harmlessness or otherwise of sharks: "Ninety-nine times out of a hundred the shark has had enough (if he sees the menacing harpoon pointed at him) and flees; the hundredth time he is something to be reckoned with. On the other hand, if this same shark sees a bather breaking the surface of the water and waving arms and legs in ignorance of the dangerous locality, he may be tempted to attack him." Yet splashing about in the water is regarded by many as the surest way to frighten away sharks!

*Burke, London, 1954.

CHAPTER XI

WHALES, SEALS AND WALRUSES

THE whale shark has no special connection with whales, except that it competes with them for the title of the world's largest creature. The use of the word "whale" in its name is misleading—the word simply means "great", as it is often used in other connections, and the term "The Great Shark", although less often used to describe the fish, is the one that will be used in this chapter to prevent confusion.

It is certain that either the great shark or the blue whale (sometimes called the sulphur bottom) is the biggest creature in the sea. Whichever holds the honour automatically becomes the largest in the whole world, for the largest land animal (the bull African elephant, standing eleven feet at the shoulder and weighing seven tons) is only a fraction of the size or weight of either.

Many authorities unhesitatingly vote for the blue whale (*Balaenoptera musculus*) as the world's largest creature. Specimens have been recorded up to a length of 108 feet, weighing 131¼ tons—figures which certainly make those relating to the African elephant look insignificant.

Specimens of the great shark have measured 100 feet —but so little is known of it, that it is at a great disadvantage when comparisons are made between it and the blue whale. Many thousands of observations of the blue whale have been made to get the figure "108 feet", but only a few of the great shark to get the figure "100 feet". Taking available statistics, the *average* length of the great shark is greater than that of the blue whale—which some authorities give as seventy or eighty feet, and some as only sixty feet. We cannot dogmatize—the question can only be settled by further investigation.

Apart from size, the great shark and the blue whale have little in common. The former is a fish, the latter is a mammal. Both are regarded by zoologists as "harmless"—but again, we know so little of the great shark's habits that the word, in its case, means nothing, while the fact that the blue whale lives mainly on tiny creatures and is apparently not aggressive does not mean much: we should perhaps say "harmless if not attacked".

Sharks can remain under the surface for any length of time without coming up for air. Both whales and sharks are absolutely helpless on land, although the whale is a breathing animal. But the whale, unlike the shark, is also helpless if it remains too long under the sea—it suffocates. So far as our knowledge goes—and it is of course limited regarding the habits of whales when far from land or shipping—whales can stay under water for as long as one hour and forty-five minutes. When the whale rises to breathe it "spouts" or "blows". This action is often described as the expulsion of water taken in at the mouth: it is nothing of the kind. The whale has a nostril on the highest part of its head, and through this it breathes out forcibly when it comes to the surface, expelling air, not water, although the expulsion causes a jet of water vapour to rise above the surface of the sea. Man's knowledge of the whale shark is so meagre that stories of its harmlessness may one day be regarded as worthless legends. Its huge transverse mouth is certainly capacious enough to receive a man. Its throat is larger than those of other sea monsters—even larger than the throats of other sharks within whose stomachs the bodies of humans have been discovered.

Whatever may be the truth regarding sharks and their contacts with divers, even the most ferocious of them are mild and gentle compared with the killer whales.

These are, beyond question, the most cruel, voracious and bloodthirsty of all swimming creatures; and we shall see that their chief victims are other species of whales. Man has waged ceaseless war against whales for centuries but anything that he has done in attacking and killing them cannot compare with the savage assaults of the killers, which had been going on for eons before man appeared on the earth, and which continue incessantly with undiminished fury.

The killer whale is a large porpoise, of the family *Delphinidae*, and constituting the genus *Orcinus*—it is sometimes called the orca or grampus. They reach a length of about twenty-five feet and are therefore smaller than many of the whales that they attack. The head is rounded and the lower jaw a little shorter than the upper. The dorsal fin is remarkably high in the adult males, and resembles a huge broadsword, nearly vertical and about six feet from base to tip—in the female it is prominent but shorter. The colour is peculiar—black above and on the fins and white below, but the white of the belly extends forward to the end of the lower jaw, and upward on each side where it forms a large, oblong, white area. Above and somewhat behind each eye is another conspicuous white spot, also oblong. In the young the white areas are tinged with yellow. The upper and lower jaws of the killers are armed with stout, powerful, curved teeth—anything from forty to fifty-six of them.

Other cetaceans—members of the whale family—feed chiefly on plankton and do not eat other whales. But the killers, hunting in packs, feed upon warm-blooded aquatic animals, and mainly on young seals, porpoises and the larger whales—in short they are cannibals, eating their own kind. In one instance the stomach of a killer was found to contain the bodies of thirteen smaller porpoises and fourteen seals. The best known species, *Orcinus orca*, inhabits all seas. Another species in found in the South Pacific. Others have been described with doubtful validity.

This preliminary description of the killer whale gives us a mental picture of whales as monsters of the sea who are attacked from without and within—*by man*, in his continuous slaughterings of them for the valuable commercial products which they yield, and *by their own kind*, the killers, which are even more ruthless and bloodthirsty.

Working in packs, like the wolves of the sea that they are, the killers will chase a school of porpoises or a huge group of eels and work their way through it, from the rear to the front, voraciously eating numbers of their victims as they proceed. They will violently attack and smash small boats, and devour anything that falls into the water from them. On some occasions they have split ice-floes a foot and a half thick by striking them with their heads and backs.

John Craig and Ernie Crockett, two fishmen with exceptional experience as underwater hunters, were shooting undersea pictures near a grotto coral formation in fifty feet of water off Cedros Island, shortly before the last war, with the aid of a Mexican named Antonio, when they had an uncomfortable experience with a killer. Crockett was down under, wearing a helmet which gave him telephonic communication with the other two on the surface. Suddenly, the Mexican turned to Craig with an ashen face—he was wearing the phone headpiece—and said, "Johnee, he's got a killer whale!" Craig, kneeling there on the deck, could hardly believe it. Killers seldom came near the shore, except when very hungry. But Craig looked down towards the beach and saw a herd of seals there—he realized the Mexican's words were true.

Crockett had gone into the cave, and had been exploring it with his underwater torch when the mouth of the cave had been suddenly darkened. He turned round. Blocking the entrance was a full-grown killer whale. The entrance was narrow and Crockett had only just managed to squeeze through some minutes before. The killer could only get his snout through, but he retreated again and again and hurled himself forward, trying to smash his way in; and kept biting at the coral to try to enlarge the opening.

Meanwhile Crockett discussed the situation with those above. They told him to remain calm and wait for the killer to go. After a while the beast did leave. Those on deck saw him break water 150 feet away, to "blow". He had a four-foot dorsal fin. Craig's worst fear was that the animal would see Crockett's air tube, which led from the sea on to the deck. If it had, it might have rushed madly at it and bitten it through—killers have shown an uncanny understanding of the purpose of air-tubes on many occasions—resulting in Crockett's death underwater or horrible mutilation if he had risen to the surface.

But the killer seemed unaware of the tube—he dived and came up to "blow" several times, and seemed to be waiting for Crockett to emerge. Craig decided that if he could only drive the seals from the beach into the water, the killer might follow them. He jumped into a skiff and pulled for the shore—not a little nervously, for he knew the killer whale's fondness for upsetting small boats. Others on the ship were waving frantically to distract the killer's attention from Craig. He reached the shore and the seals, panicking, threw themselves into the sea.

At that moment the killer came up for another "blow" —saw the seals diving in and shot at them like a thunderbolt. In less than a hundred yards' run he had snapped three of the seals in halves and had them inside him, scarcely slackening speed as he gulped them down. The herd of seals zigzagged desperately—curved, retreated, rushed on—trying frantically to escape. The killer got a few more as the herd raced out to sea, never relaxing the chase until all had vanished towards the horizon.

They phoned down to Crockett and told him to come up. He slipped the catches on his shoe-weights, inflated his diving-dress, and rose to the surface, forgetting the rule that he should not rise faster than his bubbles. He hit a corner of the boat as he touched the surface, stunned himself, and was unconscious when they got his helmet off. His first words were—in gasps—"Why the—h-hell didn't you—send me down a camera?"

The killers have not the slightest fear of humans; whether men are swimming naked on the surface, wearing Aqualungs in the under-waters, clothed in diving-suits, riding the sea in boats or standing on the shore. They hurl themselves at man whenever they have the chance. Compare their aggressiveness with that of some (not all) species of sharks.

There are numerous instances of humans riding sharks of the more harmless varieties. It is a common practice along the shore-lines of some tropical countries.

Probably few people have come into closer contact with sharks than John Brandon Siebenaler and his wife Marjorie. When he married her he promised her that they would have their own private sea. He fulfilled his promise a few years ago, and built his dream aquarium on a 600-foot stretch of Fort Walton Beach, Florida, as a commercial proposition—the "private sea" being at specified times open to the public. The venture, Gulfarium Ltd., cost an initial half-million dollars. It was stocked with 10,000 miscellaneous fish—an open-air pool surrounded by wire fencing. The aquarium's battleship-like structure was opened in August 1955.

The day came when Siebenaler wanted sharks. He took his wife out in his catchboat, with a small crew, and rounded up five sharks. Swimming among them, Siebenaler seized each shark by its fins, caressing it in his arms, and steered it into a holding tank, in which they were all brought ashore and put into the aquarium.

Four of the sharks died shortly after. They had not been injured in any way. Siebenaler said, "They died of fright—or maybe from the emotional shock of being touched by a human being." Mr. and Mrs. Siebenaler spent the whole of one night "walking" the fifth shark—going to and fro with him the whole length of the tank, caressing him and trying to coax him out of his state of nervous shock. But they could not overcome his fear with all their kindness—like the other four he died of fright.

Siebenaler declared that it was the usual story of sharks in aquariums. Other fish settle down and get used to their keepers and their surroundings. Sharks never lose their fear of human beings and few last longer in aquariums than several weeks.

Whales—and the term includes dolphins and porpoises—belong to the order Cetacea. Dolphins and porpoises (including the narwhal with its curious single tusk) have been described in an earlier chapter, among creatures which leap from the sea's surface. There are three sub-orders of the Cetacea: *Mystacoceti*, including all those whales whose teeth are rudimentary and useless and are replaced by whalebone, or baleen; *Odontoceti*, which includes all whales having teeth—sperm whales, killer whales, porpoises and dolphins; and *Archaeceti*, the extinct whales. Dismissing the third class as of little interest to us in this chapter, we confine our survey to the typical whales of the first two sub-orders, the baleen or toothless whales, and the toothed ones.

Whalebone is the material in a whale's jaws which enables it to strain its food. It is formed as a development of the ridges, often horny in character, which are found on the roof of the mouth in all mammals. It takes the form of triangular plates, which differ greatly in size, proportions and colour in various species. Plates to the number of two or three hundred are attached to their bases transversely on each side of the whale's mouth. They are smooth and straight on the outer edges but the inner ones are fringed with bristle. These bristles become matted together, forming the meshes of the whale's "sieve", with which it is able to strain from the sea-water which floods into its mighty mouth the small fish and planktonic creatures upon which it feeds. The water is squeezed out through the baleen strainers by the action of the whale's tongue.

Baleen is widely used commercially, owing to its great lightness, strength and flexibility, the ease with which it can be split, and its power to stand high temperatures without change. "Whalebone" is a misleading term, for the substance is not bone; nor is it fin, as implied in the commercial term "whale-fin". It is an epidermic (or skin) substance closely resembling hair in its nature. One of its most ancient uses was in the making of helmets. In the course of history it has been used for whips, surgical instruments, for adding gloss to certain kinds of cloth, for umbrella frames, and in countless other ways, not forgetting the use which its name immediately suggests: for those compressive devices of the late nineteenth and early twentieth centuries which kept the feminine figure within fashionable limits.

The tongue of a whale, which it manipulates so efficiently in association with its enormous strainer, is the greatest of all tongues—those of whale sharks, elephants and all other big animals are insignificant appendages compared with it.

A whale killed in 1932, which weighed 119 tons and was 89 feet in length was found to have a tongue weighing 3 tons 3 cwts.

Although the general form of the whale is fish-like, we have only to consider the characteristics of fishes—in all their diversified forms, sizes and colours—to realize that it is not a fish but a mammal. It is as much a mammal as a horse, a cow, or man himself. It is in fact a mammal which has become adapted to living in water, but it still retains its mammalian characteristics: for it has warm blood, breathes air with its lungs, suckles its young at the breast, and has the hairy covering possessed (sparsely or thickly) by all mammals. Its tail is not placed vertically, as in fishes, but horizontally—a position which accords better with the animal's need to keep rising to the surface for air. Its external fish-like form is perfectly suited to its life in the sea, but that does not make it a fish, any more than an ape's general resemblance to a human form makes it a man.

A bat is a mammal, not a bird—it has none of the characteristics of a bird, except its bird-like shape. A great part of its existence is spent on the wing, but it remains a mammal in the air, even as a whale remains a mammal in the sea.

If the whale was covered with hair, even sparsely, it might interfere with its rapid movement through the water. Its upper-lip and chin whiskers are among the few hairs on its body which link it with mammals of all kinds, from walruses with their bushy whiskers and coverings of short, closely-compressed hair, and polar bears with their thick fur coats. To keep it warm, even in icy seas, the whale has, in place of hair, a thick layer of non-conducting material—its blubber. Its fore-limbs are mere paddles, with little power of motion except at the shoulder joints. But beneath their smooth and continuous outer coverings they possess all the bones, joints, and even most of the muscles, nerves and arteries of the human arm and hand. Buried deep in the interior of the animal, and now quite useless to it, are rudiments of limbs corresponding to the hind-legs of the higher animals.

Whalers recognize several groups of baleen (or whale-bone) whales, to which they have given such names as right whales, humpbacks, finners or finbacks, and sulphur bottoms, although the latter is really a kind of rorqual. The right whales are heavy and compact in form, and are built for cruising about slowly in search of the small floating invertebrates which are their main food. The humpbacks are bulky but uncouth—heads broad and rounded in front but flat on top, with rows of hemispherical tubercles—they can attain a fair speed, due to the length of their flippers.

The finners, or rorquals, which are built for speed, and which prey largely on fish which they have to chase and catch, are the ocean greyhounds of the baleen whales. Their bodies are long and streamlined, and their necks partially mobile. The typical finback—the most commonly observed and best known of the finners—ranks next in size to the blue whale. Its shape is extremely attenuated. The adult individuals sometimes reach a length of eighty feet. Finbacks are remarkable for their assymmetrical coloration: the whale's back is grey, striped longitudinally with white, and the lower jaw is also white on one side only.

The sperm whale (*Physeter macrocephalus*) is a member of the toothed whales (*Odontoceti*), the second division of the Cetacea, and the division which comprises porpoises, dolphins (including the killer whales), and bottlenosed or beaked whales.

Fully grown the sperm whale reaches a length of sixty feet. The female is much smaller.

The head of the sperm whale is immense, although all whales do not have large heads in proportion to their bodies. It is shaped like a great elongated wedge, with the thicker end uppermost and the edges and smaller end rounded. The blowhole is single and situated at the end of the snout on the left side, and the lower jaw is very narrow and much shorter than the upper. The two sides of the lower jaw are joined together anteriorly for about one-half the length. It has rudimentary upper teeth. The lower ones (forty-four in number and cone-shaped) fit into pits in the upper jaw when the mouth is closed. The face of a whale might be best described as that of a creature with a left nostril only, at the top of its nose, a receding chin, and something resembling a hare-lip.

The back of this whale with a small fin, is raised in a series of low irregular humps posteriorly. The pectoral fins are broad and about six feet long. Sperm whales occur in all seas except the Arctic and Antarctic, but they are essentially creatures of the tropics. Sperm whales swim in herds or schools which are much diversified in character. Some comprise only young males; others females and their young led by one old bull, as a kind of "schoolmaster" or mentor; others consist entirely of old males. These old bulls do not always swim together. They are often encountered wandering singly, as if they had lost all interest in their fellow creatures. They are ill-tempered and very pugnacious, and do not hesitate to attack the boats of the whalers.

The sperm whale feeds mainly on big squids. Its great strength and powerful under-teeth enable it to dislodge them from their rocky retreats at the bottom of the sea.

The bottlenosed whales comprise four or five genera of small whales—none of them exceed forty feet in length. They are toothed, like the sperm whale, but never have more than four teeth (regularly implanted in their jaws) although some species have numbers of tiny rudimentary teeth, which seem to be useless, imbedded in their lips. The head of all the forms, at least in the young, is pointed. In the bottlenosed whale of the North Atlantic the forehead gradually increases in size with age, so that the creature literally grows a beak, strong and narrow and somewhat resembling the shoulder and neck of a bottle: a development which gives the animal its name. The beaked whales of other genera are much less abundant. They travel, both in groups and in pairs.

One bottlenose, described by John Hunter (the British anatomist and surgeon who did valuable work in his investigation of the structure of whales) was caught above London Bridge in 1798, having wandered far from its native waters.

The beluga, or white whale, is another toothed whale: one of the dolphin family, closely related to the narwhal. Its body is only from twelve to sixteen feet in length, but has graceful proportions, and a creamy-white colour: it is in fact the most beautiful of all whales. The flippers are short, the head is arched and sinks abruptly to the creature's short, rounded snout. Its teeth are small and conical, and number eight to ten in each jaw. This whale has been successfully kept in aquariums.

The white whale's headquarters are around Greenland, but they occur all over the Arctic seas, often going as far south as the St. Lawrence. Only very rarely do they appear near the British coasts. The Greenlanders capture them by harpooning, or with strong nets. The flesh is largely eaten, the blubber yields a very fine oil, the skin is made into a tough and durable leather, and other parts of the body are also used commercially. The name "beluga" is also applied to a great Russian sturgeon, while the name "white whale" has been popularized by Hermann Melville in *Moby Dick*. But the great white whale which he describes as the object of Captain Ahab's obsession is a sperm whale—a freak in its colouring—and must not be confused with this much smaller whale, the true white whale or beluga.

The great sperm whale sometimes performs gymnastics on the surface of the sea which, considering its enormous weight, are little short of miraculous. When it "breaches" —the word used by whalers to describe its leaping from the water—it shoots up twenty feet or more, and falls back flat on the surface. Another whaling word is "lobtailing", which describes the way a sperm whale stands on its head, which of course is submerged, and smacks the surface of the sea sharply with its huge tail. The percussions are thunderous and can be heard for miles around. A third peculiarity of the sperm whale is called "milling". The whale, suspended on the surface of the sea with its head projecting, turns round very slowly, again and again, with its small pig-like eyes scanning the horizon as if watching for any approach of danger.

When whales put forth their full strength they are capable of astounding feats. The explorer Captain H. G. Melsom was once hunting whales off the coast of Siberia. He harpooned a blue whale. The monster ran out three thousand feet of line from the ship. This was the limit, but the ship held fast and the captain ordered full speed astern to try to hold the whale back. The great animal scorned the power of the ship's engines. It towed the vessel *forward* at a speed of never less than eight knots (nine miles an hour) for over seven hours before it tired, and was at long last dispatched.

Some of the sleigh dogs of the Scott Antarctic Expedition were standing on an ice-floe when they were attacked by killer whales. The killers, fortunately, launched their attack from under the ice, upwards towards the dogs. The ice was two and a half feet thick, but the killers broke right through it, and the dogs only narrowly escaped destruction. The famous Antarctic explorer, H. G. Ponting, was once nearly killed by other whales of the same species, which smashed at the ice on which he was standing with terrific force.

Spermaceti is the solid constituent of the crude oil of the sperm whale and some other cetaceans. It is a white waxy substance which is extracted by draining off the oil and then washing it again with boiling water and potash. The head of the sperm whale, between the skull and the integuments, is a large "reservoir" of semi-solid head-matter which is rich in spermaceti, but the substance is also contained in the oil of other parts of the body and in the animal's humps. Mainly cetyl palmitate, spermaceti is white, pearly, semi-transparent, and lighter than water, in which it is insoluble. It has no taste or smell. It is used for making candles of standard photo-metric value—that is, for comparing the illuminating power of artificial lights—in the dressing of fabrics, in medicine and surgery (particularly in the making of ointments) and in cosmetic preparations.

Ambergris is a fatty gummy substance, the origin of which was once much in doubt. It is usually found in lumps, floating on the sea or cast up on the world's shores. Much of it comes from the coasts of the Bahama Islands, but it is also brought from the East Indies and the coasts of Africa, Brazil, China and Japan. It gener-ally contains black spots, which appear to be caused by the presence of tiny beaks of the cuttle-fish *Sepia octopodia*, the principal food of the spermaceti whale.

Some odd stories were told by the ancients regarding the origin of ambergris. One ancient speculator on the subject, Klobius, recites no fewer than eighteen theories. Paludanus and Linschotten described it as a kind of bitumen, which worked its way up through the waters from the bed of the sea. They did not suspect any con-nection with the whale, nor did numbers of other writers seeking an explanation.

Some writers believed it to be the excrement of a bird, named by the inhabitants of the Maldive Islands the *Anacangrispasqui*, which had been melted by the sun's heat, washed off the shore by the waves, and swallowed by whales, who returned it to the sea as ambergris. Others, particularly the orientals, imagined that it sprang from the sea-beds in fountains. Others declared it to be a sea-mushroom, torn from the bottom of the sea by tempests. Others affirmed it to be a vegetable product discharged into the sea by trees which had their roots turned towards the water. Others again maintained that it was formed from the honeycombs of bees which had their nests among rocks of the shore.

At the beginning of the nineteenth century, Mr. Neumann, chemist to the King of Prussia, investigated all the theories and gave it as his opinion that the bituminous one was the most strongly substantiated. One of the very oldest theories, current among seafaring people thousands of years before Neumann and his survey of the numerous conjectures of his time, was much nearer the truth: that ambergris was the excrement of the whale.

The truth is that it comes from the intestinal canal of the whale, being thrown up from its stomach. It is also taken from the bowels of sickly whales after killing them. It then has a soft consistency and a disagreeable smell. On exposure to the air, however, it gradually hardens and acquires its peculiarly attractive fragrance, which makes it an article so precious to makers of perfume. In Europe it is now entirely confined to perfumery, but at one time it was used both in cookery and in medicine, in Britain and on the continent. It is still used in these connections in the East.

Although modern reference books give one hundred pounds as the limiting size of the lumps of ambergris which are found floating on the sea's surface, much larger masses have been secured. The stuff fetches considerable sums—even a hundred years ago it was priced at five or six pounds an ounce. Realizing that money was worth far more two or three centuries ago, some of the old finds were certainly fortunate ones.

One lump of ambergris, taken from the sea near the Cape of Good Hope in the latter half of the nineteenth century weighed three hundred pounds. Another, found at about the same time, is recorded in books of the period as having a weight of fifteen thousand pounds, but in this case the size is quite evidently exaggerated, and reliable details are not given in the various accounts. Allowing for exaggeration it probably weighed several hundred pounds.

The largest lump of ambergris found floating anywhere in recent centuries with a well-authenticated weight, was bought from the native king of Tidore (an island of the Malay Archipelago) by the Dutch East India Company for eleven thousand dollars in 1694. Checked regarding its shape and size by many authorities, it measured two feet in diameter and weighed exactly one hundred and eighty-two pounds. Its subsequent history is obscure—the Company probably broke it up and made a large profit. While it was still intact the Duke of Tuscany offered fifty thousand crowns for it—an immense sum in those times.

Classification of creatures of the sea has always been more or less arbitrary, and a matter of convenience. Some animals might be classed with those in a particular group for excellent reasons, yet might, for equally good reasons, be placed in another group. The seals and walruses have many characteristics which separate them completely from whales. Seals are of the order *Carnivora*, and so are walruses, but some authorities include both in the sub-order *Pinnipedia*, while others separate them and place the walrus in a family of its own, the *Trichechidae*.

It is all very confusing to the layman, who sometimes finds it hard to understand why seals, as sea creatures possessing resemblances to whales, should be sharply separated from whales and classified with cats, dogs, lions and bears, in the order *Carnivora*, despite the fact that many whales are carnivorous and have the rudiments of land mammals in their structures.

Again, both seals and walruses are pinnipeds—having feet resembling fins—and one might feel inclined to agree with those authorities who keep them together in the *Pinnipedia* sub-order. There is one way in which we can cut this perplexing knot and get the whale, the seal and the walrus together into one simple classification: They form a group which distinguishes them from other creatures of the sea, for they are all water-living mammals: land creatures which have adapted themselves to the sea. Seals and walruses find a place in this chapter (despite the fact that they are not of the whale's order,

A shark brought ashore at Keel Harbour, Achill Island. The size of this shark—and that of its enormous mouth—can be appreciated by comparison with the man in the background.

A remarkable photograph of a live octopus.

(*James Carr*)

A photograph of a dead octopus—the kind one would prefer to meet—showing the curiou funnel: used for expelling water for propulsive purposes, also for extruding clouds o "ink", as the animal escapes its enemies.

(*Black Star*)

Cetacea) because they are air-breathing animals, with mammalian characteristics, which share certain common similarities and characteristics.

Seals are excellent swimmers and divers, and are so much at home in the sea, depending entirely for their sustenance on living prey captured in the water, that their universal habit of resorting to beaches, rocky elevations or ice-floes, to bask in the sun, sleep, or for the purpose of bringing forth their young is a remarkable one. Whales seek the shore-waters to copulate and deliver their babies, but these acts take place in the water, and it is in the water that the mother whale suckles her babies at her breast. The seals, therefore, in their habits, are not such marine creatures as the whales.

The Alaskan seals, *Callorhinus alascanus*, spend most of the year in the eastern Pacific Ocean. Yet they travel periodically to one specific place, far from their hunting grounds, to bear their young: the Pribilof Islands in the Bering Sea. They are guided there by the same mysterious instinct that directs the eels to the Sargasso weed and the salmon to their breeding places high up the rivers.

Unlike some other sea creatures, which are monogamous, the large male seal forms his own harem of several females, each of which presents him with one baby yearly. The United States government rightly controls the seal's breeding grounds, and only allows the excess young males to be slaughtered for their fur—otherwise fur-bearing seals would soon be exterminated.

The supraorbital processes of the seal's brain are well developed, in fact it is a highly intelligent animal in many respects. The external ear is either wanting altogether or very small—yet the seal has remarkably good hearing. The upper divisions of the limbs are shorter than the lower, and do not project beyond the body's skin. Each limb has five toes, and these are webbed. There is a short tail. Some seals are habitual stone-eaters, and their stomachs are often found to be partly filled with stones, sometimes fairly large ones. The seal's breathing is extremely slow. When on land and fully active a period of about two minutes elapses between each intake of breath and the next. It can hold its breath for long periods—a man would die in a quarter of the time that the animal can completely suspend its breathing. This breath-suspension power is of great use to the seal in pursuing its prey. It has been known to remain under water for as long as twenty-five minutes.

The seal's nostrils can be completely closed, making them watertight. So with its small hearing orifices. Its eyes have remarkable optical peculiarities, enabling them to be used with equal efficiency both under water and above the surface.

Seals are usually grouped under two dissimilar types, the so-called fur seals and the hair seals. The former may remotely resemble bears, and are in fact often called "sea-bears". The fur seal yields a valuable fur, but the hair seal has no fur—its hide is used for leather and its body yields a valuable oil. The hair seal inhabits the Antarctic, North Atlantic and Arctic oceans, although small groups are scattered over the globe. The fur seals are more or less widely distributed throughout the southern seas. The hair seal cannot walk or run on land—it can only wriggle on its stomach—but the fur seal can run or lope along the ground with considerable rapidity.

The brown seal has a way of sleeping that is, to say the least, extraordinary. R. M. Lockley, studying seals in aquaria in Germany, watched a pair of seals of this variety sleeping in a glass tank containing about six feet of water. The female closed her eyes first and was soon fast asleep, on the floor of the tank, her breathing suspended. After some moments the bull fell asleep, closing his eyes and nostrils and slowly sinking to the bottom. The cow seal then rose to the surface, with scarcely perceptible movements of her flippers. Her eyes were fast closed as she surfaced and began to "blow". She took sixteen deep breaths and then slowly sank again with her nostrils closed. Lockley timed their periods underwater and found that the seals often remained down for five or six minutes. They took anything from twelve to twenty breaths while on the surface. Sometimes they coincided in their ascents and descents: sometimes they alternated with each other. They slept soundly all the time.

Most seals are gregarious, and are usually quite harmless, timid, even affectionate animals, although the old males will sometimes fight each other ferociously. They are greatly attached to their young ones. They have all their five senses remarkably well developed, and a sense of balance far more sensitive than most other animals, or even man himself. They have a rudimentary speech sense, and can express themselves in various ways, varying from harsh grunts and barks to plaintive bleats. They are strongly attracted by musical sounds.

Probably no other animal, with the solitary exception of the dog, shows such affection towards man, or is so easily trained. They are the very opposite of sharks in this respect. The Siebenalers did everything possible to eliminate the deadly fear which almost paralysed their sharks when they touched and caressed them. They were using the only possible method of reassuring and taming the animals. Birds feel fear when humans contact them; so do many other creatures. But such reluctance to make friends can be overcome in all kinds of creatures by kindness. With their sharks, the Siebenalers found it hopeless —the fear gulf was far too wide to be bridged.

Right at the opposite pole are the seals. They respond so readily to affection and love to be petted and fondled. Sometimes their affection for man can become embarrassing. This was instanced as recently as July 1957, at British resorts around the Norfolk coast.

During the warm weather which occurred in the early days of that month, seals started coming ashore from the breeding banks. Posters urging holiday makers "Don't pet the seals" were put up by the R.S.P.C.A. at many resorts. Mrs. Jean Mudie, R.S.P.C.A. secretary at Hunstanton, told the London *Sunday Express* reporter that no fewer than fifteen baby seals had come ashore during the previous three days, but did not want to return to the sea again. Mrs. Mudie explained that "On shore they don't live more than a fortnight". As sea creatures they needed to return to the sea. Yet the animals were so responsive to the pettings that they would not leave the shores, and so—with the sea waiting to receive them back again—they died.

There are numerous stories of the sagacity and skill of seals. They are often seen in circuses and stage-shows performing balancing tricks. They have been trained by showmen in many countries from time immemorial. During the nineteenth century the French were particularly successful in training them, and numbers of performing seals were appearing in fairs in all parts of France.

During the 1860's a very fine sea-bear (*Otaria ursina*) attracted crowds to the London Zoo. It is not one of the easiest seals to train, being one of the furred seals which are "bearish" in both senses of the word, possessing some of the characteristics of bears and also showing signs of temper at times. This "talking fish" as it was called was a bad-tempered, even vicious, brute before a Frenchman named Le Blanc began its training. The animal, showing none of the normal seal's inclination to friendliness, savagely resented the training and attacked Le Blanc again and again. He bore numerous scars until the end of his life.

At last he won it over by persistent kindness, and it became one of the finest performing seals ever exhibited in any country. Its love for its master became unbounded. It seized every opportunity of displaying its affection, and followed him everywhere. If separated from him for only a few moments it evidenced signs of great distress. It showed eagerness to obey his slightest whim; and the tricks Le Blanc taught it have probably never been equalled—such as balancing balls, bottles and other objects; climbing ladders, firing cannons, clapping its fins, putting itself to bed, and many other feats of skill. Its range of vocal sounds and intelligence in uttering them certainly made it the nearest thing to a fish that actually talked that has ever been seen. It died in 1867 through inadvertently swallowing some hooks which had been left in the fish with which it was fed.

Walruses live among the ice of the Arctic coasts. The name is a modification of the Scandinavian *valross*—"whale-horse". A full-grown male measures from ten to twelve feet, although specimens have been recorded of fifteen feet and more. There is force in the old description of the animal: "As large as an ox and as thick as a hogshead." An aquatic mammal, allied to the seals, the walrus differs from them in possessing an enormous pair of tusks, corresponding to the canine teeth of other mammals. These tusks are formidable weapons, but their principal use seems to be in digging and scraping among sand or shingle for the molluscs and crustaceans on which the creature feeds; although it is said they also use them to hook themselves up onto the ice. Like the seal, the walrus is a stone-swallower—some writers say that it is to give them a sense of fullness when very hungry.

The greatest enemy of the walrus, next to man, is the polar bear. Fights between the two beasts are frequent, and many full-grown walruses carry marks of such conflicts. Yet the walrus is otherwise a quiet and inoffensive animal, loyal to its mate, tenderly careful of its young—it will fight to the death to protect them—and capable of "domestication" if this is begun early enough.

To the Eskimo the walrus is a prime necessity of life. There have been cases where hundreds of Eskimos have died because the walruses have forsaken some particular district. From its skin the Eskimo makes the coverings of his kayaks, or canoes. The bones furnish him with the runners for his sledges, and the heads of his weapons. The tusks are used as points for spears and harpoons, and also cut up to make bird-slings. The animal's intestines are made into light garments, or split into twine of great strength. The flesh supplies the Eskimo with food, and the abundant fat gives him fuel for his lamps.

The manati (often anglicized as "manatee") is the most curious of all the whale's cousins. The Spanish colonists of the West Indies called this aquatic mammal the *manattouï*, and this became latinized as *manatus*, meaning "furnished with hands", referring to the curious hand-like form or hand-like usage of the Manati's fore-flippers. The animal is somewhat whale-like in shape, having an oblong head, a fish-like body, and a shovel-like tail; while it has a face which can only be described as comical. Its upper lip is cleft and each of the lobes so created is separately movable. The nostrils are two slits at the end of its fat muzzle which resembles nothing so much as the conventional "toper's nose" of cartoon characters. The eyes are extremely small. The creature has no external ears. It has no tusks—the face is babyish although it has an odd suggestion of chronic alcoholism—but it has about twenty pairs of peg-like teeth in each jaw.

From the shoulder-joint downwards the manati's flippers can be moved in all directions: its "elbows" and "wrists" are peculiarly flexible. In feeding, the manati is almost human in its actions, conveying its food to its mouth with one "hand", or both simultaneously. It uses its flexible lips in an action which recalls the movements of a caterpillar's mandibles in nibbling a leaf.

All trustworthy observations show that the manati—unlike other aquatic mammals such as the seals—has no power of voluntarily leaving the water. It is a mammal which has gone into the sea in past ages, yet cannot leave it again, even for brief visits to the shore.

Many authorities believe that the sirens and mermaids of legends and fables were what we now call manatis, walruses and seals, to which the imagination of the ancients gave irresistible beauty and charm, as half-women, half-fish. But the manati—and for that matter the walrus and the seal—are among the ugliest of mammals, and it is difficult to imagine how it could be mistaken for any lady of exquisite beauty, as the typical mermaid or siren was reputed to be, even if such a charming creature had the tail of a fish.

The dugong, or duyong, is another of the "sea-cows". It is a marine animal and feeds chiefly on seaweeds. Some specimens attain a length of nine feet. Found along the shores of Australia, of the Indian Ocean, and around the Red Sea, it differs from the manati in having a crescent-shaped tail, and a pair of tusks. Dugongs are fond of basking on the surface of the water, or browsing on submarine seaweed pastures, for which their thick flexible lips and truncated snout fit them.

In the earlier Australian dugong-fisheries, natives were able to harpoon the animals, but the dugongs, learning by bitter experience, became wary and would not let themselves be approached. So the harpoon method of slaughter was abandoned in favour of nets. These are spread at night, and in their meshes dugongs are caught in considerable numbers.

The female dugong is proverbial among the Malays for her maternal solicitude for her offspring, of which but one is produced at a birth. Dugongs have been nearly exterminated, owing to the demand for the fine oil, which is used for medicinal and other purposes, yielded by the Australian species.

There are such remarkable differences in the structures, habits and physical appearances of whales that it is sometimes difficult to realize that they are all members of one group: yet the underlying principles of their structures are identical, and their behaviour patterns and outward forms have many correspondences. Between the great blue whale and the dugong are a range of creatures with very diversified characteristics, yet the basic relationship of them all becomes more and more evident as they are studied. They are all aquatic mammals, and so are more nearly related to man than they are to any of the fishes.

The great blue whale is probably the most typical whale of them all. Its gargantuan size is the factor in its make-up which causes us to forget our close relationship.

Some writers of books on whales have said that when they have first seen one it has been difficult to believe that it is an animal at all. The men on the *Kon-Tiki* felt friendly towards whales, seeing them at short range—but as Georges Blond points out in *The Great Whale Game,** the conditions in which the men were conducting the voyage had reduced them to something like a state of primeval innocence, and they had a friendly feeling towards the whole of creation.

Man's wholesale slaughterings of all the various kinds of whales threatens them with extinction. International conferences have not always resulted in whole-hearted co-operation by the nations' whaling industries: agreements have been ignored and some nations particularly fail to adhere loyally to the international whaling convention.

One authority, Dr. Gilmore, said only last year that the California grey whale had become almost extinct twice in the last hundred years, and this is but one of numerous statements which might be quoted to indicate the extent of man's butchering of whales for commercial profit. Norwegian whaling operators particularly are seriously concerned regarding developments in the industry. Reports of the National Oceanographic Council

*Weidenfeld and Nicolson, London, 1954.

in recent years show that the world's whale population is menaced by the increasing introduction of efficient methods of whale catching. We can only hope that the international whaling agreements governing the season's catch are strictly adhered to by all parties.

Forty-five states, meeting at the International Technical Conference on the Conservation of the Living Resources of the Sea in 1955, held in Rome, agreed that measures to secure conservation should be based on scientific information; that such conservation should be brought about by conventions between states; and that there should be international co-operation in scientific research—*but* in subsequent sessions jettisoned its own proposals by agreeing that coastal states could adopt conservation measures unilaterally.

Strongly reminiscent of world conferences on disarmament, all such meetings fail to achieve their purpose while individual nations persist in policies based on their own selfish interests. The official world figures of whaling results from 1946 to 1955 tell their own sad story. Man is increasingly exploiting whale-slaughter for profit, blind to the fact that he is gradually exterminating the animals which bring him that profit.

During the year 1946–47, 23,043 Antarctic pelagic whales were slaughtered; 2,550 Antarctic South Georgia whales; and 9,227 elsewhere than in the Antarctic. With only two or three fluctuations, the figures have steadily increased, until the latest available ones in each category are Antarctic pelagic (1954–55) 34,388; Antarctic South Georgia (same period) 3,266; and elsewhere than Antarctic (1953–54) 16,391—an increase of 19,125 whales in the total figures (over a third more whales slaughtered) in the ten years.

The whale is now profiting man increasingly during its lifetime, as scientific facts gained from its structure and habits are applied to the welfare of mankind. A typical instance of this is the scientific expedition which sailed into the lonely waters of Mexico's Scammon Lagoon (half-way down the Pacific coast of Baja, California) early in 1956, with an extraordinary objective: the venture was organized to record the heartbeat of a whale.

The National Geographic Society, the Douglas Aircraft Company, the Sanborn Company of Cambridge, Massachusetts, and many other organizations and individuals had given generous aid. The expedition's ultimate purpose was to contribute something to man's investigations of the mysteries of the human heart, which is roughly the size of man's two fists and beats from fifty to ninety times a minute, compared with the heart of a whale, which weighs more than two hundredweights and beats far more slowly—perhaps fewer than ten times a minute.

In 1916 a young Boston cardiologist, Dr. Paul D. White, had dissected the heart of a sperm whale, and published the first detailed scientific description of it.

The mammalian heart—in the mouse, the man, the elephant and the whale—beats constantly because of the electricity it generates within itself: its driving impulse or current in the human heart being no more than a thousandth of a volt. The Scammon Lagoon expedition failed in its objective, but it had gained valuable knowledge regarding its shortcomings. Applying that knowledge towards the perfection of their investigational methods, and not in the least daunted, Dr. Paul Dudley White (who is President Eisenhower's heart consultant) is returning with his colleagues to the Lagoon this year.

Man's contact with the whale is therefore not always tinged with cruelty: it may be that his investigations are in some way benefiting the animal itself.

CHAPTER XII

THE DRIFTING SWARMS

WHEN, in the middle of the last century, Johannes Peter Müller (1801–58), the German physiologist and comparative anatomist, developed a method of straining plant and animal life from sea water with a fine net, he was only doing what the whale had been doing for countless centuries, and far more efficiently. But Müller opened up a new world of teeming life: the world of plankton.

Naturalists in many countries were quick to realize the possibilities of the new realm's exploration. It was as if mankind had remained in almost complete darkness regarding the constitution of the oceans and had emerged into blinding light. To realize what had happened one should try to imagine a world in which man knew nothing of insects, having investigated the structures and lives of all kinds of animals in complete ignorance of the fact that ants, bees, butterflies and similar creatures existed: and had suddenly discovered the insect kingdom, with its swarming millions of curious and colourful life forms. For the world of plankton is at least as large as the insect world, and its inhabitants are at least as diversified.

Collections of plankton were at first made in the more easily accessible shore-waters. Müller's researches attracted the attention of the scientific world, and stimulated interest in the plankton, but he was not the first to investigate them, nor even to use the tow-net in securing specimens, although he is stated to be the first user of the net in nearly all modern text-books on oceanography.

J. Vaughan Thompson, the brilliant British amateur

naturalist, had used a tow-net to collect plankton from the sea off Cork, as early as 1828, when serving as an army surgeon in Ireland. He was the first to describe the zoëa—the crab in its early planktonic stage. He discovered the true nature of barnacles a little later, in 1833. He was the first to reveal to the world that plankton are not exclusively tiny creatures that are permanently afloat, but contain many animals from the sea-beds in their early larval stages, and that such sea-bed animals send up their babies in clouds, to be scattered far and wide by ocean currents, just as plants on land send their seeds into the winds for distribution.

Darwin, eleven years before Müller, used a tow-net on his voyage in the *Beagle*—a fact recorded in his *Journal of Researches* under the date 6th December 1833. T. H. Huxley also used a tow-net on H.M.S. *Rattlesnake* within a year or so of Müller's use of the device. It was then a simple enough appliance: a small bag of fine muslin or silk gauze, usually attached to a collecting jar, towed through the water on a line behind a boat.

Even as early as the middle of the eighteenth century— a hundred years before Müller's use of the tow-net to catch plankton—two Italian zoologists, Count Luigi Marsigli, pioneer in oceanography, and Vitaliano Donati, naturalist and traveller, had invented and used the naturalist's dredge: a coarse net on an iron frame which brought to the surface from the sea-bed many forms of life previously unknown.

Four years before Müller's use of the tow-net, Edward Forbes, who became the recognized pioneer in planktonic research, had begun his dredging, in British waters and in the Aegean Sea. All the nets used in these earlier explorations, and all the devices which have developed from them, are man's imitations of the whale's *baleen*— the flakes or "blades" of which, with their fine hair-like filaments, are the most efficient sieve for the collection of planktonic creatures that nature has devised.

It may be difficult at first to realize that the microscopic plants which are comprised within the plankton form a vegetation which is sufficient to support the entire animal life of the sea, but this is indeed the case. Invisible to the human eye, although their presence contributes to the colour of sea water, all the vast hosts of planktonic creatures—numbers of them almost invisible to the eye —depend upon such microscopic plants. So, directly or indirectly, do all the invertebrate animals of the sea-beds, all the myriads of shoals of fish in the sea, in their infinite variety, and all the aquatic mammals, including the greatest sharks and whales.

One of the most remarkable facts in oceanographic science is the paradoxical one that the whale—one of the largest, or it may be the largest, creatures in the sea, feeds on some of the sea's smallest creatures, using its wonderful sieve to extract them from the water.

The microscopic plants in the plankton are largely diatoms, dinoflagellates, blue-green algae and similar lowly organisms. Victor Hensen (1871–1911), the German physiologist, who is credited with devising the name "plankton", began his study of the biology of drifting life of the ocean with the theory that a conical silk net with meshes of a particular size would catch *all* the plants in the cylindrical column of water through which it passed. He thought that if he counted, under a microscope, all the plants in a unit of sea water it would be possible to calculate the number living below a unit of the sea's surface. But Hans Lohmann quickly pointed out to him that very small, and highly important, members of the phytoplankton (planktonic plants) were passing through the meshes of the very finest silk nets.

From that moment special filters were devised, which have been continually improved. Man searches deeper and deeper into the infinitesimal, both in the structure of atoms and in the world of planktonic creatures.

The microscopic plants known as diatoms are so

numerous that they are now recognized as the most important plants of the sea. Each diatom is a tiny pill-box—or perhaps "jewel case" would be a better description. They occur in an infinite variety of forms, numbers of them singularly beautiful. The living contents of a diatom are enclosed within two similar valves of silica, which fit tightly together like the top and bottom of a box. Myriads of the tiny siliceous "boxes" form the main part of the oozes of the world's sea-floors, particularly in the North Pacific and the Southern Ocean. You can see and handle quantities of these microscopic cases if you obtain some ordinary fuller's earth, which consists of the cases of myriads of what were once the shells of marine diatoms, deep in the sea.

Those diatoms—the majority—which are enclosed in silicon, look like crystals under the microscope: some are shaped like rods, some like discs, some are cubes, some cylinders. Others have spines or other curious adornments: all are complicated structures of ingenious design, and many are exquisitely lovely. The smaller varieties, called nannoplankton or ultraplankton, which pass easily through the finest silk, are (according to the most recent scientific pronouncements) among the most important of all food providers.

Diatoms, like land plants, are quickened by the advent of spring, come to their most prolific activity and abundance at this time, and then decline in summer, having exhausted the mineral salts held in solution in the water around them. Eventually the surface waters of the sea cool and sink, and are replaced by waters from below which have not been exhausted of their nitrogenous and phosphoric salts. These waters from below form the new surface layer, in which new plants will flourish abundantly (though invisible to our eyes) in the following spring and summer.

Planktonic plants need to capture light energy from the sun, like all green plants on land. For this reason they float near the open sea where the rays of the sun can penetrate to them. Owing to their microscopic size they have a high ratio of surface in relation to volume, and therefore sink very slowly although they are slightly heavier than water. Small organisms, other things being equal, sink more slowly than large ones. The same is true of creatures which fall through air. As Professor Haldane expresses it in his *Possible Worlds* : "You can drop a mouse down a thousand-yard mine shaft, and on arriving at the bottom it gets a slight shock and walks away. A rat would probably be killed, though it can fall safely from the eleventh storey of a building." Diatoms which have spines—thereby increasing their surfaces in relation to their volumes—can fall even more slowly, just as the puff-balls of dandelions are able to float in the air because their surface areas are so greatly disproportionate to their volumes. Lead pellets of the same volume as the puff-balls would fall quickly.

This is the basic principle which controls the level of the diatoms in the sea, and affects their availability as food for all kinds of sea animals.

Diatoms normally reproduce by simply dividing in two, and this act of reproduction naturally affects their distance from the sea's surface. Instead of one box there are now two boxes, each containing a nucleus of living matter—protoplasm—out of which develops the new valves, or halves of the new box. The process of separation is baffling and inexplicable—as mysterious as the division of cells which results in the creation of the foetus within the womb of a woman. But there is this vital difference in the two kinds of fission. Human cells multiply as the infant is built up, but do not diminish in size. But as the diatom "boxes" multiply, some of them get smaller. The process of repeated division by forming new half-boxes *within* the old ones necessarily causes this diminution in size. Thus there is a wide range in the size of diatoms of the same species, although each individual soon attains maturity. After a certain number of divisions, what is called an "auxospore" is formed, by which means the diatom's original size is regained.

What may be termed the "pill-box" diatoms are only one kind of planktonic plant. The "boxes" are of all shapes, and not all diatoms are planktonic—there are numbers which are not "wanderers" but are motionless on the sea-beds in shallower coastal regions where light can penetrate down to them. The planktonic (drifting) "pill-boxes" are far more varied in structure, due to the vast variety of devices which assist their flotation.

Apart from the box-like forms there are diatomic plants which are suspended in the sea water by microscopic "life-belts"—tiny globules of oil. Numbers of species live solitary lives, but there are innumerable forms which live in association: linked by their valve surfaces; or joined in flexible chains by fine threads of protoplasm.

There are diatomic plants flattened like strips of paper; others which are strung together like pieces of ribbon; others which are like twisted paper streamers; others which are drawn out into very fine hair-like forms; and there are rigid needle-like forms, some of them pointed at each end. There are planktonic plants—all invisible to the naked eye—which resemble land insects, such as caterpillars.

There is one form which roughly suggests the Praying Mantis, and there are many which look like twig-imitating insects—yet all these are plants. Numbers of the microscopic plants resemble household ornaments such as vases or cups, and many of these are beautifully embellished. Myriads of the planktonic plants have flagella with which they draw or propel themselves through the water. Such creatures are enigmas, for many of them are claimed by both botanists and zoologists, and indeed, have the characteristics of both plants and animals.

When we turn from planktonic plants to planktonic animals we enter a vast world of drifting life-forms with a teeming population of living creatures millions of millions of times greater than our world of humans. Enormous numbers of these plankton feed upon the planktonic plants. The chief plant-eaters are the cope-pods, which vary considerably in size, although the vast majority are microscopic. Their numbers are so prodi-gious that any small harbour or bay contains in its sea water thousands of times more copepods than there are human beings on earth. All kinds of fishes feed on plank-tonic swarms which contain large numbers of copepods, and (like the whale) use various devices to filter them from the seawater.

Fishes cannot discriminate between the various forms of planktonic food, but in some cases the size of the planktonic animals eaten by them varies with the age of the fishes. In the earlier stages of a herring's existence, for instance, its "sieve" (the gill-rakers) is finely meshed, so that numbers of the smallest diatoms are caught in it. As the herring grows, its gill-rakers coarsen, allow-ing many of the smaller varieties to pass through them. When adult, the herring's diet consists mainly of the larger copepods and plant-feeding plankton.

As a general principle in the "feeding chain", fishes feed on copepods (planktonic animals), and copepods feed on microscopic floating plants—diatoms or other floating forms of planktonic life. A herring may have as many as ten thousand copepods in its stomach, and each of these copepods may have hundreds of planktonic plants in its own.

Planktonic animals—free-swimming sea animals of all kinds whose powers of locomotion are not strong enough to overcome the transporting forces of tides and currents —vary considerably in size. Many are microscopic, and nearly all of them are less than an inch long, in fact most of them are less than half an inch; but some of the crustaceans measure several inches, and many authorities include giant jelly-fish five or six feet across. For clearer understanding of the creatures one might divide them into *temporary* and *permanent* planktonic animals; the first class consisting of the babies of numerous sea creatures which pass out of the planktonic stage as they become adults and resist the tides and currents as burrowers, crawlers or swimmers. The *permanent* planktonic animals, on the other hand, spend their entire lives at the mercy of the waters, drifting around unresistingly, so that they never have fixed habitations or localities, and are only at rest when the waters permit them to be.

The copepods are the main group in the second class, although not all of them are planktonic, for some of them attach themselves to the sea-floor, or to rocks or sea-weeds.

Many early students of sea creatures did not realize, as they studied the tiny babies of fishes and other sea animals, that they were looking at the offspring of creatures already known to them. So they sometimes gave names to the babies of parents whom they had already named. One of these they named "zoëa"—it was a strange little shrimp-like creature, which developed into something half-way between a lobster and a crab, and was classified as two different species. We know today that both creatures are immature crabs in stages through which they must pass to become adults.

Such mistakes in classification are easy to make, especially when studying planktonic animals, for they are extremely difficult to keep alive in captivity and for a curious reason. In the sea they are "cushioned" by the waters themselves and seldom come into confined spaces. But in captivity they often bump into the glass walls of an aquarium or case and injure themselves. Others die because it is difficult to know what food to give to creatures, many of whom have mouths so small that they cannot swallow anything bigger than two- or three-thousandths of an inch across. For these reasons not all planktonic animals have been watched through their entire life cycles—and many varieties still remain unclassified, their habits and histories almost completely unknown to us.

One particular species of planktonic animal persists in baffling zoologists. Fishermen's nets occasionally bring up single specimens of this transparent, spherical animal, which has been named *planktosphaera* because of its shape. All attempts to fit it into any known animal group have failed, although it suggests relationship with several. For fifty years a solution of the problem has been sought, but (although it has been argued that the creature is a young crinoid or sea-lily) the half-inch ball of living substance has not been finally classified.

The copepod crustaceans vary considerably in size and structure, but the typical copepod is divided into the usual three regions of the crustacean-head, thorax and abdomen. The pear-shaped head and forepart carries six pairs of appendages, modified into a sensory and feeding complex. It has two antennae—very long and with many joints—"arms" which, if the creature is imagined in an upright position, hang down from its "shoulders" to below its forked or branched tail. Behind the head each of the first five thoracic segments has a pair of jointed and forked swimming legs, the movements of which carry the copepod through the water in spasmodic hops along what seem to be purposeful courses. The best mental picture of a copepod is that of a creature which looks something like an ant with no head, yet with a branched tail and two extra-long arms something like earwigs and a number of legs on either side of the forepart of its body which it uses in a series of jerks to propel itself through the water.

Many of the copepods look like small fleas; others are

the babies of jelly-fish and often resemble them; vast swarms of them are tiny shell fish of every conceivable kind. They must not be thought of as colourless, although numbers of them are transparent, for their colours range right through the spectrum. Blue copepods wear orange aprons, consisting of eggs. Attempts have been made to represent some of the ghostly, transparent forms on white paper, but against any such background they look unnatural, even when the colours are perfectly reproduced. Other attempts to present their complicated designs and remarkable colour harmonies against dark backgrounds, such as black paper, have been more successful, but even the best of them look somewhat artificial and harsh and far too solid.

It is far beyond the scope of this book to give any detailed description of planktonic creatures, whether plants or animals. Any selection of them must necessarily be very inadequate and quite unrepresentative. Investigation of them is in its infancy, but is now making progress because of the labours of numerous enthusiastic students. Among these, Dr. M. V. Lebour in England is one of the few who have been able to build up a number of life-histories regarding plankton which are invaluable to the basic research which has already been given to the creatures. But all the knowledge already attained is but a drop in the ocean compared with what remains to be known about these wonderful sea plants and animals.

Hilary B. Moore, Professor of Marine Biology of the University of Miami, U.S.A., and one of the world's leading authorities on plankton, has said: "As usual, the more we study these animals the more problems they present."*

*Article on plankton in the *National Geographic Magazine*, July 1952.

CHAPTER XIII

THE SINISTER CEPHALOPODS

UNTIL squids can be observed more closely in their natural surroundings, man's knowledge of them will necessarily remain limited, but enough is known to justify belief that they are among the most extraordinary of all sea creatures.

They are the most numerous of all cephalopods, which are the most highly organized of all molluscs. Cephalopods are therefore relatives of the oyster, the snail, the winkle and the whelk. All molluscs are invertebrates—backboneless animals to which the majority of all living species belong: backboned creatures like man himself forming only five per cent of the whole.

All molluscs have soft spineless bodies, partly covered with mantles of skin. Nearly all of them are shelled animals, and the gastropods have toothed ribbons which vary considerably in structure but are similar to the whelk's rasp strip with its replaceable teeth.

The cephalopods we know today are found in abundance in all the world's seas, yet their numbers have diminished considerably since primeval times, when there were far more in the oceans. It is probable that only a small minority of them became fossilized, so that the fossil records, preserving vestiges of more than 10,000 species, give us only a partial and fragmentary conception of the enormous number of species which swarmed in the oceans before man.

There are now only about 650 species of cephalopods known to us. Considering their ancient lineage they are appropriately blue-blooded, due to the presence of a copper-containing compound in their blood which causes the colour, even as the characteristic colour of man's blood is caused by the presence of the iron compound haemoglobin in the red corpuscles (*erythrocytes*): five millions of them in every cubic centimetre of the fluid. Man's red blood corpuscles are individually a pale greenish-yellow, but in dense masses, the *erythrocytes* colour changes to a distinct red, even as cephalopodan blood is a pale clear blue when deoxygenated and a rich dark blue when oxygenated.

Squids are the most colourful of all cephalopods in more ways than one. The bodies of some species are covered with numbers of tiny pigment spots. When expanded at the will of the squid, by the use of numbers of microscopic, fast-acting muscles, the animal is given its characteristic colour. But when the squid wants to make itself inconspicuous it can use the muscles to contract the pigment spots, with the result that the creature virtually disappears from view without moving.

Although less efficient than that of the common cuttlefish, the squid's skin-mechanism outdoes the chameleon's in the rapidity of its colour changes. The vanishing trick just described is one of the two methods which the squid uses to elude its enemies. The other is well known, but seldom fully understood: its swift use of jet-propulsion.

Squids are masters of this vanishing trick—they draw water into their body chambers, which are lined with powerfully-muscled walls. Suddenly, the water is expelled so violently that the escaping stream makes the squid's body shoot backward. This is one of the squid's normal modes of progression, but if it wants to escape from danger it can release a stream of blinding ink. This extraordinary fluid is discussed at considerable length in Frank W. Lane's authoritative and invaluable work *Kingdom of the Octopus*,* the first book on the octopus and

*Jarrolds, London. 1957.

similar animals to be published in the English language for over eighty years.

The cephalopodan ink-sac is the subject of a classic study by Paul Girod, published in France in 1882. It is a small, pear-shaped organ situated between the creature's gills, and ends in a long neck which leads into the funnel-like aperture from which the ink is discharged. The ink, or sepia, is possessed by nearly all cephalopods. Only the nautilus and some octopuses that live in the deep seas are without it. It is a thick, black gummy fluid that has been famous for writing purposes from time immemorial. Ink from cephalopods which died and were fossilized millions of years ago can be liquefied from its dry state and used for writing today. The substance owes its blackness to melanin, the abnormal development of a dark pigment in the hair, feathers, skin, etc., of animals, as opposed to albinism. Thus the cephalopod's sepia is associated with one of mankind's most crucial problems, racialism, for it is related to the pigments in the skins of the coloured races.

The colour of the ink varies with different species. The late Ronald Winckworth, a British expert on the Mollusca, described it as sepia-brown in squids, blue-black in cuttle-fish and jet-black in octopuses, but its basic substance in all cases consists of pigment granules similar to those which develop in the melanocytes of the human epidermis, and in enormous quantities in the skin of the negro.

We read in the ancient satires that the Romans used sepia as an ink. Cicero calls it "atramentum". The Chinese, many thousands of years ago, used it as ink, and Chinese ink is still noted for its blackness today. Pliny declared that sepia was the blood of the cuttle-fish. Rondelet (1507–66), famous for his investigation of the fishes of the Mediterranean, stated that it was the cuttle-fish's bile.

Numerous writers in modern times have said that

cephalopods use their ink to create a kind of underwater "smoke-screen" under cover of which the animal escapes its enemies—but this is only a half-truth, or over-simplification of the facts. Cousteau, who has witnessed more cephalopodan ink-discharges than most men, says in describing one of his experiences: "We found that the emission was not a smoke-screen to hide the creature from pursuers. The pigment did not dissipate: it hung in the water as a fairly firm blob with a tail, too small to conceal the octopus. . . . The size and shape of the puff roughly correspond to that of the swimming octopus which discharged it."

Frank Lane rightly quotes the suggestion that the octopus or other cephalopod discharges its ink, not as a smoke-screen, but to confuse its attacker by creating a semblance of itself. We might take the squid as an instance of what happens. Menaced by the approach of an enemy, the creature suddenly *paints a picture of itself* in the water—Cousteau's words show that this is no exag-geration—and while its attacker's attention is diverted to a "shadow squid" the squid uses its complicated muscles to close the pigment cells on its body-surface, so that it vanishes from sight and makes off, leaving its attacker concentrating on "a fairly firm blob with a tail".

If necessary the squid can eject "ink forms" several times in succession so that its attacker would be deceived into rushing towards one phantom after another, while the real squid, at a safe distance, quickly assumed its normal appearance.

Eels are much excited by the presence of sepia in the water. They dash wildly about seeking their ancient enemy. Denis L. Fox, the American biologist, once offered a moray eel, that he had in a tank, a mussel removed from its shell. The eel refused it, but when Fox dipped it in some octopus ink it was greedily swallowed.

Two other experimenters—the MacGinities—put a

moray eel into a tank with a mud-flat octopus: one of the eel's favourite dishes. The moray eel's sight is poor. It started searching for the octopus, but the latter quickly discharged its ink. Long after the ink had dispersed (although traces of it remained, much diluted, in the water) the eel persistently searched for its enemy, but the ink in the water was evidently having a most remarkable effect on the searcher. The eel would go right up to the octopus again and again, touching it with its nose, yet showing no excitement and obviously unaware that it was in contact with its prey. It may be that one of the purposes of the ink is to paralyse the olfactory sense of the cephalopod's enemies, and that they are unable to attack it without olfactory stimulation. Certainly large numbers of octopuses and their kind are saved from destruction by eels—which are their main predators—by discharging their inky fluids. Yet in strong concentration the ink is fatal to its owner: a fact proved by naturalists who have caught small octopuses and put them into buckets; after which they have annoyed them so that they have discharged their ink into the sea water in the buckets. Every time the experiment has been made the octopuses, surrounded by their ink in strong concentration, have died in a few minutes.

Oceanic squids vary from small, luminous deep-sea species to huge creatures many feet in length. The giant squid (*Architeuthis*) may grow to a length of fifty-seven feet, with tentacles extended. Squids have eight arms (like octopuses) but also two tentacles. The terms "arms" and "tentacles" are often confused. The Octopoda have eight arms only. The Decapoda (which include squids and cuttle-fish) have eight arms plus two tentacles.

The brain of the common octopus is well developed (for the animal possesses far more intelligence than is usually supposed). Certain nerves control the flow of water into and out of a cavity in the mantle.

Relaxing and contracting these mantle muscles, which bathe its gills, jets of water pass into and emerge from the cavity. Using these streams of water the animal breathes and moves. When lazily resting or moving slowly through the water, the mantle circulation is gentle, rhythmic and slow. But when alarmed or excited the mantle muscles work rapidly, driving out jets which give the creature quick and easy movement. When the squid points its funnel forward it moves rapidly backwards, and when it wants to move forward it turns its funnel back on itself.

The funnel then shoots streams of water backwards past its moving body, sending the animal forwards quickly in bursts of speed. Cephalopods like the octopus and squid are not the lazily moving creatures that they are often thought to be. The speed of an octopus, swimming steadily, has been timed as about the same as a human swimmer—four miles an hour, but they can dart about like lightning when chasing their prey or eluding their enemies.

The quick movements of these creatures are due to the high development of its giant nerve-fibre system. In the mantle are comparatively large nerve-fibres as well as numerous smaller ones, and down all these fibres pass the inconceivably swift impulses from the brain which galvanize the muscles into action. So well-developed is the cephalopod's nervous system that reactions to external stimuli are far quicker than those of many other sea animals.

The suckers along the arms of the cephalopods are marvellous examples of natural mechanisms. Each consists of a muscular membrane, reinforced around its rim in some species. The centre of each sucker operates like a piston, so that as it is raised a partial vacuum is created within the sucker giving it a powerful grip on anything to which it is attached.

Carrying out tests with a spring balance, G. H. Parker

discovered that a sucker with a diameter of one-tenth of an inch—slightly larger than a pin's head—needed a pull of two ounces to detach it, while one with a diameter of a quarter of an inch required six ounces. A large octopus has about 240 suckers on each of its eight arms, making a total of 1,920. This means that a force of 720 lb. (more than a quarter of a ton) would need to be applied to break the hold of a common octopus with a span of five feet, and even greater force to detach one of the bigger creatures, the arms of which would probably tear away first, leaving the suckers still attached.

Aquarium officials have sometimes under-rated the power in an octopus's arms. On one occasion at the Brighton Aquarium, before precautions were taken, an octopus pulled up the waste-valve of a tank during one night, releasing all the water, so that the tank contained only a mess of dead octopuses in the morning.

The octopus uses its suckers to explore surfaces, or the body of its victim, a fact which shows that they are not merely gripping devices but sensitive organs. Having gripped its prey, the animal can kill it in either of two ways, by means of its rounded beak or by administering poison. The former method indicates that the creature has an uncanny knowledge of just the right place to use its powerful sharp instrument as it holds any particular animal.

When not in use the beak is retracted and hidden, but as the octopus pinions a crab (for instance) in its deadly stranglehold, it turns the crab so that its abdominal plates are towards its mouth and dispatches the crustacean quickly with a sharp crunching action.

With many octopuses poison is used, and when this happens (again taking a crab as an example) the victim is seized and drawn into the parachute-like membraneous folds of the octopus's web, where the poison is injected. The venom is mainly secreted from the creature's posterior salivary glands, and kills the victim in a few minutes. It is more virulent in the common octopus than in the cuttle-fish and in common squids, in which the glands are smaller. In eating a crab the octopus shows some skill and discrimination, usually pulling off the back first, eating the viscera and then discarding the back, after which it pulls off the legs one by one, cleaning them out and dropping them one by one until the meal is finished.

Cephalopods do not always have it all their own way—they are sometimes killed by the shellfish that they attack. Even large octopuses may get one or more of their searching arms gripped between the shells of a clam. It has been said that fierce struggles sometimes develop between cephalopods and giant shellfish. But the chief enemies of many of the best known species of octopuses are eels—some of the morays and congers having powerful bodies and stiletto-like teeth. When a large eel finds a small octopus it swallows it whole. But if the octopus is a big one the monster eel may use a different technique: forming a loop with its tail, and sliding its head (wrapped in its foe's arms) backwards through the loop, thus forcing the arms off its slippery body—and all the while gulping the octopus farther down its throat. Sometimes a conger or moray eel may bite off one or more of the writhing arms, if the octopus gives it an opportunity.

Squids can apparently travel much faster than octopuses. Lane, who has assembled numbers of remarkable facts regarding the speeds of all kinds of living creatures, estimates that (judging by evidence available) large squids can race through the water at speeds up to twenty miles an hour.

The flying squids of the genus *Onychoteuthis* are so described from their habit of leaping from the sea. They pump sea water into themselves and release it in forceful streams until they attain a considerable speed. The flying squids of the genus *Onychoteuthis* are said to unfold pieces of their webs like wings, and steer themselves up to and through the surface of the water, sailing through the air for considerable distances.

The American marine biologist, George F. Arata, Jun., was on board the U.S. Fish and Wildlife Service ship *Theodore N. Gill* when he made an unusually close observation of a flying squid's "take-off". The squid was only about six inches long, but observational conditions were ideal. The squid was first seen just ahead of the ship. It had just struck the water after a flight, and rested motionless until the ship was only ten feet from it—it then darted to one side, turned swiftly and leaped *backwards*, sending out a jet of water from its funnel. By this time its fins were fully extended, and its arms bunched together to form a kind of hood. The creature sprang into the air and flew diagonally across the ship's bow for at least fifty feet before making a flat "belly-landing" on the sea's surface. There was no wind whatever to assist its flight.

Squids often fall on to ships' decks. On one occasion W. H. Rush was on a ship three hundred miles off the coast of Brazil, when a shoal of hundreds of squids flashed out of the sea, rose to a height of fifteen feet and landed on the ship's deck, which was twelve feet above the surface.

Numbers of the adult cephalopods seem to live (at least during the day-time) some hundreds of feet below the surface of the sea. Compared with the coastal forms or the flying squids, which live partly above the surface, the deep water squids and octopods show a reduction and simplification of their bodies to withstand the enormous pressure. In most deep-sea species the muscular systems and ink-sacs may be only weakly developed, or the ink sac may be entirely absent, but in all such creatures there is a corresponding increase in the amount of the gelatinous tissue underneath the skin.

This gelatinous tissue is a remarkable substance, for it

gives the cephalopods not merely the base for their muscles but also the "cushioning" that they need to resist the pressures of the depths. It also has buoyant qualities. It is found in many of the planktonic groups and nekton, in nemertean and annelid creatures, in the angler-fishes, and in the larvae of fishes like the eels, apart from its presence in cephalopods. One of its extraordinary characteristics is its compressibility. Cephalopods might be appropriately described as the Houdinis of the seas. They are not only performers of vanishing tricks, but are escapists of no mean ability.

N. J. Berrill tells the story of a naturalist who had caught a small octopus, about two feet in length, and had confined it in a wicker basket, which he took on to a street car with him. Ten minutes later there were screams from the other passengers. The octopus had squeezed itself through a crack *only a half-inch wide* and had crawled on to the lap of a lady, who was in hysterics.

The word "compressible" assumes startling significance when applied to cephalopods. Experiments made with them have elicited facts regarding their remarkable powers that really justify such adjectives as "fantastic" and "sensational"—even that most misused of adjectives of modern times, "fabulous".

Roy Waldo Miner, at one time the Curator of Living Invertebrates in the American Museum of Natural History, was collecting specimens with a companion near some coral reefs in Puerto Rico, when he captured a small octopus, the body of which was about two inches long, although with its arms fully extended it measured about a foot across. Miner had an empty cigar box handy and he put the creature into it, tucking in its eight arms. The octopus was a tight fit in the cigar box. Miner put on the lid and secured it by hammering in a number of tacks, and tying some stout cord around it several times. Houdini himself was never fastened into a box more securely or tied up more carefully than that octopus.

Miner put the box into the bottom of the dinghy which he was using, and went on with his work, collecting specimens. When he landed, he picked up the cigar-box, which was still securely tied, and prized open the lid, to show the octopus to his companion. The box was empty.

Miner said later that he felt he had been tricked by some piece of parlour magic, or that a miracle of some kind had happened. But as he stood there, completely baffled, Miner looked down into the boat, and there among the bilge water was the octopus, looking up at them with its almost human eyes, from under the blade of an oar. They quickly recaptured it. The extraordinary creature had inserted the sensitive tips of its arms into the thin crack along one edge of the cigar box below the lid, and—getting a purchase by gripping the outside of the box—had, in Miner's own words—"*pulled its rubber-like body through the crack by flattening it to the thinness of paper.*"

The account of this extraordinary incident might seem incredible if related by anyone else, but Miner's reputation as a competent researcher in natural history phenomena compels belief: and there are other incidents which provide confirmatory evidence of this remarkable compressibility of the octopus.

Frank Lane records the experience of C. W. Coates, of the New York Zoological Society in this connection. Coates sent ten small octopuses to New York in cigar boxes—received from a collector for the Society in Key West. What happened makes it abundantly clear that the octopus definitely possesses the extraordinary power indicated in Miner's account. Quarter-inch holes were drilled in the ten cigar boxes, and each box was tightly bound with fish-line before they were placed in the shipping tank. The fish-lines tightened in the water—the boxes were submerged in the tank—and when they were tested afterwards it was found absolutely impossible to prise up any lid as much as an eighth of an inch. Yet every one of the ten octopuses squeezed itself through. They were all found in the shipping tank, free of the boxes. Coates has also stated that when common octopuses *with a three-foot span* were sent from Florida to New York enclosed in wire netting with a half-inch mesh, they regularly squeezed their way out to freedom—each creature passing through one of the half-inch apertures.

The octopuses which effected their escapes in such an amazing fashion were relatively small specimens of their kind, but it is difficult to understand how they could squeeze their two-inch bulb-like bodies, together with their fleshy arms, through such thin cracks or small apertures, for their organs are complex and their eyes are sensitive instruments.

There are midget octopuses only two inches in length. At the other end of the size scale are the common octopuses of European and West Indian waters (*Octopus vulgaris*) which have arms five feet in length, giving the creatures a spread of more than ten feet, while the monstrous octopus of the Pacific (*Octopus hongkongensis*) sometimes attains a diameter of no less than thirty-two feet. When two octopuses fight, their arms become entangled in seemingly hopeless confusion as they strike at each other with their fearsome beaks. The excitement which they suffer on such occasions causes their colour patterns (which are normally mottlings of brown, tan and yellow) to become more vivid, while waves of red, violet, blue and purple successively suffuse their bodies, sometimes creating violent colour contrasts. But when the creatures are crawling over sandy stretches their colours fade to greyish-white or pale tan, so that their bodies harmonize with their backgrounds and they become practically invisible.

There is a cephalopod which moves about in the shallow water of the coral reefs of Bermuda which is called the dancing octopus. Its brown body, spotted with white, is gracefully balanced upon long slender arms, and the creature waves these like a pirouetting fairy, only occasionally touching the sandy floor with their tips.

Perhaps the most remarkable of all the cephalopods is the argonaut, or paper nautilus (*Argonauta argo*) an animal so exquisitely beautiful that it seems quite unrelated to the octopus, yet its eight arms and other characteristics indicate their near kinship. Its delicate and fragile paper shell, or "boat", is famed in legend, song and story.

The poetical ideas which clustered around the nautilus during classic times and in the Middle Ages were as mythical as they were romantic. Until the middle of the nineteenth century the argonaut or paper nautilus was a baffling mystery, for although the creature was known to be a lady, and always mentioned as "she", no one had the faintest idea how the animals reproduced themselves, for no one had ever seen a male.

In 1827, Stefano delle Chiaje discovered a small creature—it looked like a parasitic worm—attached to an argonaut. A few years passed and the great naturalist Cuvier examined five more worms and concluded that they were parasites, constituting a genus quite unknown to science. Each of these "worms" resembled the arm of a cephalopod—it was about five inches long and had a number of suckers, varying from about fifty to just over a hundred. Cuvier named the new genus *Hectocotylus*—"the arm of a hundred suckers". Other naturalists and biologists examined the "parasite" in after years, but none suspected the truth and the dual mystery remained: "Was there a male argonaut?" and "How did the creature reproduce itself?"

The Swiss biologist Albert Kölliker began an intensive study of the "parasite" and published papers in 1845 and 1846 in which he pointed out that the "worm" had a small cavity in which he had found sperm cells resembling those of a cephalopod. By 1849 Kölliker had convinced himself that he had found the male argonaut, for he pro-

I

fessed to find, and actually drew and described, the digestive, circulatory and respiratory organs of the "parasite"—parasite to him no longer.

Kölliker's error is perpuated for all time in the *Hectocotylus octopodis*, which is not an animal at all, for as was subsequently shown it does not breathe or eat and has no heart.

Heinrich Müller (1820–60), the celebrated German anatomist, solved the dual problem in 1853. While working in Messina he examined a number of very small argonauts which had no shells and were a different shape from any he had hitherto seen. He found among the arms of each specimen a sac that when opened contained a coiled *Hectocotylus*. This was at last seen to be the modified sexual arm of the male, which breaks off and stays in the female.

The female's body measures up to six inches across, with arms stretching out from it varying in length up to eighteen inches long, so that the creature has a span of anything from two to three feet. This means that the beautiful shell which contains the body would also be anything up to twelve inches across. But the male is a tiny creature compared with its mate. It has a little thimble-shaped body with a mantle less than a quarter of an inch long, while its arms are about half an inch in length. The body of the female often has a diameter twenty times that of the male—a difference in size which might be illustrated by comparing a coco-nut with a small marble. In the male argonaut the sperm duct is in its third left arm, in a tiny sac. This eventually bursts and from within it the *Hectocotylus* unwinds until it attains a length of five inches—ten times the length of the male argonaut himself. Very little is known of the details of mating, but the elongated third arm certainly fertilizes the female, either while attached to the tiny male or after it has broken away. We do know that the female often carries the male around with her, tucked away in her shell.

After the male's third arm, the *Hectocotylus*, has broken away it certainly has power of free movement, for specimens have been observed winding and twisting about in water very actively. Kölliker's error was pardonable, for the detached arm acts very much like a worm—much as a living creature with its own individuality.

The "shell" of the female argonaut is not a true shell, but really an egg-case, formed between the oval expansions terminating the creature's first pair of arms. The arms are held together and a gelatinous substance gradually develops between them which is finely moulded on the inner surface of its membraneous expansion and which slowly hardens in the water to a spiral paper substance, exquisitely embellished with parallel ridges of delicate texture. The two halves of the "shell" are joined along their lower edges to form a "keel" which is decorated by a double row of brown knobs which are spaced to correspond with the suckers of the arms.

During the lifetime of its owner the "shell" is elastic and yielding. If carelessly grasped by anyone its extreme thinness and fragility cause it to crumble like extremely thin egg-shell.

Two of the female argonaut's arms are greatly dilated at their extremities. It was once generally believed that she used these arms as sails, raising them high above the shell, so that the wind filled them and she was driven along by it, while she directed the course of her lovely ship by paddling with her remaining arms, which hang over the side of the curious craft like oars. In consequence of this belief the creature was named the argonaut.

Certainly she carries a precious cargo. For the female argonaut herself, inside the shell, is a most beautiful creature, despite her seemingly unattractive form. The animal—called the "poulp"—is superficially no more than a shapeless mass, but it is a mass of silver with a cloud of rose-coloured spots. A long semi-circular band of ultramarine blue is clearly marked at one of its parts—along the "keel". The lady is entirely enclosed in her abode, and it has been doubtfully reported that she leaves the craft to forage about in its neighbourhood, propelling herself by her siphon like any ordinary cephalopod.

Within the shell she lays her eggs, already fertilized by the male, and these are suspended in a grape-like cluster attached to the interior of the spire. If she is swimming around outside the shell and is attacked she gets back into her shell like lightning to protect her eggs, curling herself inside her strange craft until almost hidden.

The real purpose of the expanded arms is to cover the exterior of the shell, and to build up its delicate structure and repair any damage to it: the substance of the delicate shell being secreted by these arms. The lady uses them to mould the substance into shape, so that (despite their clumsy appearance and apparent simplicity of structure) her arms are used like the hands of a sculptor.

To obtain a mental picture of the nautilus looking out of her home, think of some large sea-shell that you have seen—one with graceful ridges—and give it graceful lines and artistic embellishments. Realize that this shell is made of extremely thin material, and then imagine a curious "face", in profile, protruding from it—its main characteristic being a perfectly round staring eye. Instead of a nose or chin, imagine a number of slender, tapering appendages projecting from the "face", held closely together and rippling slightly as the creature stares at you. There you have the paper nautilus guarding her eggs— one of the sea's most beautiful creatures, on acquaintance, although not at first sight.

The paper nautilus, or argonaut, must not be confused with the pearly nautilus—an entirely different creature. Many legends describe the pearly nautilus "sailing the seas", and how she will "spread the thin oar and catch the rising gale". The fact is that (unlike the Portuguese man-of-war) she is really a bottom-of-the-sea species that hunts for shrimps and other creatures on the ocean floor. True, she has sometimes been seen on the surface—a pearly, colourful ship of great beauty. But whenever this happens she is in a weakened condition, and it is possible that she only comes to the surface to die.

Monstrous squids certainly exist, but their terrifying characteristics—their writhing arms, their cruel beaks, their staring almost-human eyes—have created mightier and even more malicious monsters in the imaginations of seafaring men. One of these mythical creatures was the kraken.

The term, of Norwegian origin, applied to a fabulous creature of the sea, is now assumed to apply to a gigantic squid which has risen above the surface again and again in past centuries. It may or may not be a species known to us, for there are probably more animals in the ocean deeps than those described in our natural histories.

The kraken was first described by Pontoppidan, Bishop of Bergen in Norway, but numbers of writers of older accounts gave descriptions of similar monsters. Summarizing details of many accounts, the kraken is supposed to lie deep down in the sea "in eighty or a hundred fathoms of water", and always at some leagues from land. Very rarely does he rise to the surface, but when he does he looks like an island several miles in circumference, with enormous mast-like arms with which he wrecks ships as if they were floating match-boxes, and creates enormous whirlpools. The kraken's form has been described as like that of a crab. His tentacles or arms are reputed to be hundreds of yards in length: with them he snatches up ships, or men who have jumped in terror from them, and carries them down to his rapacious maw under the waters. Sailors of many countries have described him as larger than any whale, shark or octopus. Time alone will tell whether there is any truth in the suggestion that he and other monsters like him lurk far down in the dark waters of the ocean deeps.

CHAPTER XIV

ILLUMINATING THE OCEANS

THERE are three main ways in which squids produce light: through bacteria in their bodies, by secretion, and by means of photophores or luminous organs.

There are many squids inhabiting shallow water which have luminous bacteria living in glands beneath their mantles. These amazing glands have lenses and reflectors and exist for the sole purpose of producing light. Each of these squids has a built-in rear-light, with a magnifying optical system—and it uses light-producing fuel for hours without need of recharging. The Japanese authority on luminescence, Yata Haneda, states that "the light is continuous yet controlled by a thin film of ink about the glands".

Luminous bacteria are quite different from the ordinary luminescent species of bacteria which live on the skin of some marine animals. A creature known as the lantern squid uses these bacteria, also the *Spirula*—a cephalopod belonging to a genus having a flat spiral shell in the hinder part of the body. Johannes Schmidt observed a *Spirula* several times which emitted a pale yellowish-green light. The spirula's lamp, unlike others, burns continuously without fading. It is an organ which has a diaphragm above it which automatically switches the light on and off.

The squid *Heteroteuthis dispar* is sometimes regarded as a deep-sea species, but it has been brought to the surface from depths of only four hundred or five hundred feet.

These tiny squids (which are among the plankton) are often caught up into surface waters by currents and sometimes cast ashore. It is a squid which produces light by secretion. A gland near the ink-sac stores the substance in abundance, in a reservoir from which it is extruded by muscular contraction whenever the creature wills it. The animal usually produces no light until disturbed, but immediately it is touched it shoots out a stream of mucus, which is known as luciferine. This, as it meets oxygen in the water, creates a chain of brilliant bluish-green points of light—rod-shaped light-particles which glow brightly for some minutes.

There are at least two other squids which produce light by secretion. Cousteau and Houot were down 3,500 feet in the French Navy's bathyscaphe F.N.R.S.3, in 1953, when a squid about one and a half feet long appeared in the field of their searchlight. It shot out a blob of what appeared to be white ink, but when the searchlight was switched off the extruded secretion glowed with a phosphorescent light. As the men watched they saw two other squids discharge similar luminescent clouds.

The third way in which squids produce light is by microscopic organs called photophores—organs which are covered with a layer of chromatophores. These are normally expanded so that they completely cover the photophore, but when they are contracted at the will of the squid then light is emitted. The number of photophores possessed by squids varies with the species—some have less than twenty. There is one species, *Nematolampas regalis*, which measures only a few inches across, and has nearly a hundred photophores: five on each eye, ten within its mantle, and seventy on its arms and tentacles.

One Mediterranean squid has nearly two hundred photophores. Some squids have them only on their eyes and on some of their arm-tips. Others have them over many parts of their bodies. One squid, *Vampyroteuthis infernalis*—one of the most sinister names given to any sea creature—has two near the base of its fins which have eyelids or shutters which can be opened and closed. Some squids have transparent windows through which the light from their photophores streams out. Other squids have internal photophores, giving light within their bodies. Others have photophores on eyeballs which are on the ends of stalks—appliances which combine range-finders with their searchlights.

The fire-fly squid probably possesses the most efficient light-producing equipment of them all. Although a deep-sea creature it comes to the surface to breed, each year from April to June, in Toyama Bay in the Sea of Japan. It is only four inches in diameter, but it has three fairly large photophores on each of its arm-tips, and on two of its arms numbers of photophores along their entire length. It also has hundreds of photophores scattered over its mantle. Thus equipped the fire-fly squid flashes its lights periodically, as though it were signalling to other creatures. The flashes vary in length and rapidity. The arm, mantle and eye photophores can flash together or separately—they give out the brightest light. The photophores on the arm-tips can flash all together or separately. Science remains in complete ignorance regarding the purpose of the lighting equipments of some of these squids.

The emission of light by living animals is a widespread phenomena, which becomes limited to special parts of the body in higher species. Many of the coelenterates show tendencies towards such localization. In medusae the whole body surface may be luminous, but the light may be brighter along specific areas, such as the radial canals, in the ovaries, or in the marginal sense-organs. In certain polyps there are eight luminous bands.

Creatures of the genus *Pyrosoma* are joined in free-swimming colonies in the form of hollow cylinders, closed at one end. *Pyrosoma* (a creature of tropical seas) is responsible for some extraordinary displays of phosphorescence. Each creature in the floating colony has two small patches of light-producing cells at the base of a tube, which when stimulated discharges light. At the point of irritation the individuals begin emitting light and (as if the remaining members of the colony were responding to the signal) the light spreads until all the individuals are giving forth light, so that the whole colony is ablaze.

Land creatures which emit light are beyond the scope of this book—numbers of them are of course well known. But the luminous land creatures form light-giving groups which are not comparable, in numbers or in the efficiency of their devices, with the inhabitants of the sea which are able to emit floods, patches and flashes of light.

Numbers of theories have been propounded in attempts to explain the working of the mechanisms—if we can call them mechanisms—which produce the light emitted by sea creatures.

Among earlier explanations was Mayer's theory that the light from the sun is absorbed and given forth again by the organic protoplasm—a theory which contributed nothing. Brugnatelli advanced the hypothesis that the food of the light-giving animal contains light energy before being swallowed, and that, after digestion, specialized organs convert the energy into light—but he had no explanation of the functioning of the light organs. Macaire enlarged upon the presence of phosphorous and coagulated albumen. Spallanzi wrote about the oxygen producing slow combustion within the creatures, but his ideas comprised no kind of explanation.

So theories were adumbrated, modified and discarded, until Todd and McCartney advanced the theory that has been developed and generally accepted since—that animal luminosity is solely dependent upon the vital force or nerve energy acting through the nerve systems of the light-producing creatures, so that it is, under specialized forms of structure, transformed through the secretions and general tissues into radiant energy, sometimes chemically, sometimes mechanically.

Translated into more modern terms: the biochemical basis of luminescence consists of the interactions of a substance called luciferin with an enzyme called luciferase; in most organisms the presence of oxygen being needed to produce the light. It is therefore to be noted that the latest "explanations" are made in chemical terms. Little is known of the substances concerned. It is questionable whether, after over a century's intensive research into the problem, scientists are any nearer the truth of the matter. Accumulation of data does not necessarily imply understanding of the way the light-producing mechanisms work, or of their purposes.

It is of course obvious that some sea creatures which possess light-producing devices use them as snares to catch other creatures, while others use them as sexual lures to attract their mates. But such obvious explanations only account for a minority of the cases where creatures have the power to produce light. Recent research has revealed the startling fact that when numbers of mid-water nets are towed at many levels in deep oceanic waters the probability is that no fewer than *four-fifths* of the fishes taken will bear light organs. It therefore seems highly probable that deeper and deeper research into the oceans will confirm this fact and that the percentage may well become even higher.

Creatures near the surface which are reached by the light of the sun obviously do not need such organs as much as those which live lower down, where the sun's light does not penetrate. Miles down in the deeps, myriads of creatures may be using light-producing devices in ways completely unsuspected by man.

Of the deep-sea angler-fishes, two species have an

extraordinary luminous gland which they use to lure their prey. This gland, possessed solely by the females, is at the end of an appliance which can only be described as a fishing rod. The base of the rod is firmly fixed in the snout of the fish. Along the rod are two sets of muscles which are used by the fish to raise and lower the luminous bait.

It is certain that the lights are often used as warning signals to other fish. Some of the coelenterates, before resorting to pitched battles with other sea creatures, in which their weapons are their poisonous stings, use their phosphorescence in this way: it not only illuminates the surrounding region and enables them to see their foes, but also warns away others of their kind, particularly females who need to be kept out of the battles.

According to August Brauer, who made a special study of the luminescent organs of certain fish, the chin barbels of certain stomiatid groups are used as light lures. The barbels (slender tactile appendages around the mouth) are very diversified. Some are whip-like, some tassel-shaped, and the luminous organs are also of many kinds. Some have bulbs attached, which light up, others have their luminous organs within the barbels; others again have luminous traceries besides bulbs.

Brauer believed that many fishes having light organs arranged in systematic groups use their light organs in patterns to identify themselves to other creatures of their own kind—signalling, in fact, in codes known only to the members of the particular species. Such manœuvres would have special significance in the breeding season. Such signals may also be used to signal information regarding food to other fishes—the finding of food at a distance being of vital importance to deep-sea fishes.

Astronomical research had a start of thousands of years over oceanic investigation for men had been studying the stars for centuries, and had learned how to interpret the light signals from suns separated from our own by billions of miles long before (only five hundred years ago) explorers began voyages across unknown seas. Even then the depths of the oceans remained unexplored, and it was less than a century ago that science looked down into the world's waters and, as oceanic research really began, saw within them points of light which now seem to challenge the known stars in number and fascinating interest.

As we begin to realize the stupendous significance of the fact that the world's oceans are not entirely dark, but are populated, from the sea-floors of the great deeps upwards for miles, with countless millions of creatures carrying their own lamps, rivalling the known stars in number and far exceeding the lighting devices of the world's land surfaces in diversity and ingenuity, our conception of the oceans must necessarily change. They will become vast areas of increasing illumination; physically, as more and more living species are catalogued by natural historians, and imaginatively as oceanographic research widens and deepens within them.

The success of undersea exploration will largely depend upon man's use of increasingly efficient lighting devices.

In a physical sense, and also (within limits) in imaginative senses, the sea is becoming more and more penetrable. Down into hitherto unknown depths, where myriads of points and patches of light move in all directions through millions of cubic miles of dark water, man is taking his own light-producers and his own appliances to record scenes which have been registered only upon the optic retinas of fishes for eons of time.

The latest underwater lamp is one which has been developed by the General Electric Co., Ltd., in collaboration with the Admiralty Research Laboratory. The three main requirements of underwater lamps are: that they must be light, easy to handle, and simple to operate. The A.R.L.'s experiments have shown that these requirements can be met by free-flooded lamps, in which the hydrostatic pressure is resisted by the glass envelope.

Operating in direct contact with the water, their success depends on what is called the implosion resistance of that envelope—implosion being the bursting of a vessel inwards under pressure. Success has been attained with this new lamp after numerous experiments. The prototypes showed that the outer surfaces of the bulbs used were cooled effectively by immersion in the sea, but the inner surfaces were heated by radiation and conduction from the filaments, operating through the gas fillings. Bulb failures were soon found to be due to the severe thermal stresses set up within them, rather than the pressure of water from without. Using a wall thickness of about a millimetre in conjunction with a specially shaped bulb, the present lamp came into existence; one which can withstand a pressure of 650 lb. a square inch —equivalent to a depth of 1,300 feet.

As the new lamp is operated only when fully submerged, it has been possible to reduce the size of the bulb and improve its resistance to implosion; for full advantage is now taken of the cooling effect of the sea water. The connections to the lamp are protected by a sealing "muff" of moulded rubber, which helps to provide a complete lighting unit for underwater use, in conjunction with the light-weight fitting originally designed. The units first used, of which the new lamp is the latest development, were first operated in the search for the Comet aircraft which crashed in 1954. During recent trials by the diving ship H.M.S. *Reclaim* there were no failures: the exhaustive tests showing that one diver can handle four of these lamps during underwater inspection work, while directing salvage operations. The lamp can also be used for underwater television.

The lighting device just described is but one of numerous inventions perfected in recent years for deep-sea exploration, and may serve to indicate the enormous progress made in a few decades with all kinds of devices for illuminating the underwater world, and for photographing it in connection with such appliances.

Underwater cameras have been steadily and rapidly improved in the last decade. In France an underwater camera that requires no housing has passed the prototype stage and is going into production. Underwater television is developing its own techniques, and progress is rapid in the perfection of devices of all kinds to meet the needs of what is virtually a new science.

Underwater television technicians have faced and overcome problems which at one time seemed insurmountable. Making pictures under water, especially at considerable depths, requires something more than expensive apparatus: it requires nerve, endurance, and creative imagination to a degree not demanded in the setting up of land surface studios. Pioneers in underwater photography have dived to the limit of endurance to take photographs with ordinary cameras: ordinary only in comparison with motion-picture ones. Using diving-suits and Aqualungs such divers have often had their own ideas about underwater photography—ideas which have contributed much to the latest developments in underwater motion-picture equipment. Solitary cameras have been lowered to a depth of 20,400 feet, and observers using cameras have descended to 13,287 feet in what is called "the dirigible of the sea"—the new bathyscaphe.

One of the earliest uses of the television camera under the waves was in the atoll of Bikini in 1947, where it was successfully employed to register the effects of the atomic explosion. Four years later, in 1951, the underwater electronic eye justified itself triumphantly when it discovered the British submarine *Affray*, after a flotilla of ships had searched for her in vain.

Yet another advance has been made in undersea photographic equipment recently, in the perfection, by Canadian technicians, of a television camera enclosed in a steel cylinder weighing no less than two and a half tons, to resist pressure at great depths : the camera being controlled by an operator who remains on the parent ship, taking pictures under the water as the huge cylinder moves about in all directions at a speed of about a mile an hour.

Numbers of brilliant scientists like Dr. Edgerton— inventor of the high-speed electronic flash lamp, which is capable of brighter-than-the-sun exposures as brief as a millionth of a second—are now devoting their minds to problems of underwater photography.

Oceanographic science is in its very earliest infancy. All man's researches have taken him down only a small fraction of the distance that separates him from the floors of the deepest ocean chasms. The bathyscaphe descents which have already been made have penetrated the deeps at a few places only, and may be compared with the first ascents into the air in engine-powered aircraft made by the Wright Brothers. It will be some years before man's bathyscaphes (improved beyond recognition from those we know today) descend over six miles into the Mindanao Deep, and release explorers who will walk the sea floor and investigate the life-cycles of the strange creatures which live there. Yet man may well persist in the improvement of his underwater devices until he is able to make his way over the sediments which have been deposited there through uncounted eons of time.

Illumination of the oceans will continue until larger and larger areas are flooded with light. The impenetrable sea of today may be widely explored during the next few generations.

Considering the enormous advances in all fields of human knowledge in recent years, our wildest imaginative speculations regarding the future exploration of the world's seas may become matter-of-fact reality before our children's children have reached maturity. But the sea will always remain, in some senses, impenetrable. Should the entire area of the world's oceans become, at some future time, brilliantly illuminated, and all their multifarious species catalogued and described, so that no single inch of the deepest floors remained uninvestigated, new mysteries would unfold within and beyond every school of knowledge acquired. Myriads of new facts would fructify as science sent forth new exploratory roots. Growth is an eternal process which cannot be confined or ended by fruition. Impenetrable today—in the sense that it is baffling and inscrutable—the sea will remain impenetrable as long as man inhabits this spinning planet.

Sir Cyril Hinshelwood's words, spoken as President of the Royal Society in June 1957 when he was asked what was hoped to be gained from the Geophysical Year, are particularly applicable to the sea and its wonders:

If we could predict all that we would learn it would not be worth doing. The Creator was much cleverer than Man, however, and has done all sorts of things that we never suspected. Any new knowledge may produce a discovery of great value. The more unpredictable that knowledge was in advance, the greater its value will be.

INDEX

273